PACT - SLP

Language Exercises *for* Auditory Processing — P*reschool Edition* (LEAP-P)

D1192481

By

Larry J. Mattes and Patty R. Schuchardt

Illustrated by Patty R. Schuchardt and Tom Matthews

Academic Communication Associates

P.O. Box 4279
Oceanside, CA 92052-4279

Copyright © 1997 by Academic Communication Associates, Inc.

All rights reserved. Worksheet pages from this book may be reproduced by the owner of this manual for use with individual students.
These pages, however, may not be reproduced for general distribution
to an entire school, school district, clinic, or group of professionals.
No other part of this manual may be reproduced, in any form, without
permission in writing from Academic Communication Associates, Inc.

**Academic
Communication
Associates**

P.O. Box 4279
Oceanside, California 92052-4279

Printed in the United States of America
International Standard Book Number: 1-57503-032-2

TABLE OF CONTENTS

INTRODUCTION

Language Exercises for Auditory Processing – Preschool Edition (LEAP-P) includes basic language activities for children in preschool and kindergarten who have difficulty attending to auditory stimuli, recalling what was said, or understanding the information presented. Auditory processing and verbal reasoning skills that are considered important for success in the early school grades are emphasized. The activities help children focus their attention on the meaning of language as they listen to stories, verbal instructions, and other auditory stimuli. The reproducible activities can be used in regular classrooms or special education programs with children as young as 3 years of age.

The activities in this book will be especially valuable in programs for children with oral language deficits. Young children with communication disorders often have difficulty understanding basic concepts used within the classroom. They may complete classroom tasks incorrectly because they do not understand the teacher's verbal directions. These children may also experience difficulty remembering verbal instructions, especially in situations where several instructions are presented simultaneously. This book includes exercises that can be used to strengthen auditory processing skills as children respond to a variety of types of auditory stimuli.

Organization of LEAP-P

The book is divided into four sections:

1. *Auditory Processing Workout*. The activities in Part 1 of the book require children to process auditory information as they follow directions, answer questions, make comparisons, identify errors within statements, make inferences, use contextual information, and perform various other language tasks.

2. *Look and Listen*. Each of the 20 worksheets in this section includes two pictures in which a vocabulary contrast is represented. The child is asked to listen to sentences and to point to the appropriate picture. The child is also asked to respond verbally to questions relating to the nouns and actions depicted in the pictures.

3. *Story Fun*. This section includes 10 short stories that are presented orally to the child. Each story is followed by comprehension questions relating to the story events.

4. *Animal Adventure Worksheets*. All of the activities in this section relate to the pictures on 10 reproducible picture worksheets. Jason the Bear, Mary Mouse, and

other animal characters are depicted on the worksheets. Each picture worksheet shows the animal surrounded by six objects. Tasks are included in which children identify words from descriptions, listen for specific information, answer questions, "fix" sentences that contain incorrect information, and tell stories.

5. *Fun with Moods and Feelings.* The child is asked to listen to sentences and short stories in which both happy and sad feelings are conveyed. The child's task is to identify story events as "happy" or "sad." The child is also asked to fix statements that contain incorrect information about the story content.

Most of the activities in this book can be presented in a game format by placing individual task items on playing cards. Picture worksheets such as those in Appendix A can be used as response sheets for teacher-created "games" in which children follow auditory directions. Sample game cards and reproducible game boards are included in Appendix B. Additional game cards can be created using task items from the worksheets.

This book is not designed for use as a "program." The teacher or specialist should select activities based on observations within the classroom setting and data obtained from an assessment of the child's needs. If a child demonstrates difficulty recalling information presented in the classroom, for example, the teacher should select activities that require the student to recall information or to carry out specific instructions.

As children participate in the activities in this book, specific "problems" that may be affecting learning often become evident. Additional activities should be provided in these areas, using materials that are relevant to the child's interests and to the content of the classroom curriculum.

Prior to presenting the activities, it is important to identify the child's specific learning needs. Although formal tests can provide useful information, it is also important to obtain information about the child's language performance in the classroom and at home. The following questions should be considered when assessing the child's performance.

1. Is the child able to focus attention when listening to stories and oral presentations within the classroom?

2. Is the child able to remember and understand information presented orally by the classroom teacher?

3. Is the child able to follow directions in the appropriate sequence?

4. Is the child able to understand the basic language concepts used when verbal instructions are presented in the classroom?

5. Is the student able to respond appropriately to simple questions?

6. Is the student able to sequence information heard in the classroom?

7. Is the child able to listen effectively for a variety of purposes?

8. Have the child's parents noticed specific problems in attention, memory, or comprehension in the home environment?

It is important to consider how the child's performance varies in different types of learning situations. Some children, for example, exhibit poor listening skills only when they are asked to perform tasks that they do not enjoy. One should observe the child in a variety of contexts before concluding that he/she has an auditory processing "disorder."

Homework Activities

Professionals in the school environment should collaborate with parents when providing intervention programs for young children with special learning needs. With guidance from the speech-language pathologist or classroom teacher, parents should be able to administer the activities in the home environment. By reinforcing skills taught in the school or clinic, the intervention program is likely to be more effective and more efficient in helping the child to acquire new skills.

All of the record forms in this book may be reproduced for use with individual children. By reproducing the materials, speech-language pathologists, classroom teachers, and family members can work as a team in providing intervention programs for children with language-based learning problems.

PART I
AUDITORY PROCESSING
WORKOUT

The language activities in this section require the child to respond to various types of auditory stimuli as he/she answers questions, follows directions, makes comparisons, associates concepts, recalls details, etc. The activities can be used to strengthen listening, speaking, and verbal reasoning skills. Each activity is presented on a reproducible worksheet.

ACTIVITY 1 - ANSWERING YES-NO QUESTIONS

Name:_____ Date:_____

Instructions: The child is presented with the questions below. The child's task is to answer "yes" or "no."

___ 1. Are leaves blue?

___ 2. Do broken toys work?

___ 3. Do men swim?

___ 4. Do children eat cupcakes?

___ 5. Do people mow the carpet?

___ 6. Are cold days hot?

___ 7. Do people walk?

___ 8. Is baseball played in the ocean?

___ 9. Do telephones whisper?

___10. Do saws cut wood?

___11. Do cows fly?

___12. Do dogs get tired?

___13. Do passengers ride in trains?

___14. Do elephants live in nests?

___15. Do wheels roll?

___16. Do telephones drip?

___17. Do pages tear?

___18. Do slow animals move quickly?

___19. Do dentists talk?

Copyright © 1997 by Academic Communication Associates. This form may be reproduced.

___20. Do fish cheer?

___21. Do artists paint?

___22. Do books hear?

___23. Do watches tick?

___24. Do shirts dance?

___25. Do toasters juggle?

___26. Do dishes break?

___27. Do airplanes doodle?

___28. Do books read letters?

___29. Do winds blow?

___30. Do bushes sneeze?

___31. Do televisions hear?

___32. Do lizards bark?

___33. Do trees melt?

___34. Do plates clap?

ACTIVITY 2 - CORRECT THE STATEMENT (WORKSHEET A)

Name:_____ Date:_____

Instructions: The child's task is to state whether each statement is true or false. If the statement is false, the child should correct it.

___ 1. Birds have hands.   _____

___ 2. A cat is an animal.   _____

___ 3. A dog meows.   _____

___ 4. A bear has chicks.   _____

___ 5. Grass is purple.   _____

___ 6. A stove is in the bedroom.   _____

___ 7. You write with a pencil.   _____

___ 8. You walk on your hands.   _____

___ 9. A fish lives on land.   _____

___10. A triangle has four corners.   _____

___11. A carrot is a vegetable.   _____

___12. An apple is a fruit.   _____

___13. An orange is a vegetable.   _____

___14. A pear is a meat.   _____

___15. Bacon comes from pigs.   _____

___16. Beef comes from chickens.   _____

___17. Watermelon is blue.   _____

___18. Four comes after six.   _____

Copyright © 1997 by Academic Communication Associates. This form may be reproduced.

___19. A lion barks.   _____

___20. Shoes are worn on the hands.   _____

___21. Gloves are worn on the ears.   _____

___22. A ship floats on the water.   _____

___23. A rock is soft.   _____

___24. An airplane travels.   _____

___25. A person swims in water.   _____

___26. A ring is worn on a finger.   _____

___27. A necklace is worn on a wrist.   _____

___28. A clock has many pages.   _____

___29. A clock keeps the time.   _____

___30. Skates are worn on the feet.   _____

___31. You cut your shoelaces.   _____

___32. You run with your legs.   _____

___33. You sleep with your eyes open. _____

___34. You drive a car.   _____

___35. You can ride a chicken.   _____

ACTIVITY 2 - CORRECT THE STATEMENT   (WORKSHEET B)

Name:_____ Date:_____

Instructions: The child's task is to state whether each statement is true or false. If the statement is false, the child should correct it.

___ 1. You drink a sandwich.   _____

___ 2. You smell a rose.   _____

___ 3. A ball does not roll.   _____

___ 4. Hands are attached to legs.   _____

___ 5. You see with your nose.   _____

___ 6. You taste with your eyes.   _____

___ 7. You hear with your ears.   _____

___ 8. A camel has stripes.   _____

___ 9. A tiger is green.   _____

___10. A worm has legs.   _____

___11. A frog eats insects.   _____

___12. A monkey lives in the ocean.   _____

___13. You put ice cream in the oven. _____

___14. You cook in the freezer.   _____

___15. You iron with a pan.   _____

___16. A lemon is very sweet.   _____

___17. A piece of paper is heavy.   _____

___18. A feather is very light.   _____

___19. A car uses soda to go.   _____

Copyright © 1997 by Academic Communication Associates. This form may be reproduced.

___20. Rings are worn on your wrist. _____

___21. Flowers grow from the sky. _____

___22. Clouds are cotton balls. _____

___23. Cotton candy is very sour. _____

___24. You lick a sucker. _____

___25. Toes are on your hands. _____

___26. Rocks are good food. _____

___27. Celery grows into a tree. _____

___28. Bananas are a yellow fruit. _____

___29. You wear pajamas to the store. _____

___30. You use an umbrella in the rain. _____

___31. You put shoes on your head. _____

___32. You write with a ruler. _____

___33. Spaghetti is made of string. _____

ACTIVITY 3 - SILLY SENTENCES

Name:_____ Date:_____

Instructions: The following sentences contain absurdities. Have the child fix each silly sentence after you read it to him or her.

1. Ben mopped his hair.

   _____

2. Sally put orange juice behind her ears.

   _____

3. Tara wrote with a chair.

   _____

4. Chuck poured milk in his shoe.

   _____

5. Lisa ate rocks and bacon for breakfast.

   _____

6. Phil wore glasses to hear better.

   _____

7. Lynn washed her hands with syrup.

   _____

8. Betty ate a tree from her garden.

   _____

9. Carlos read a radio.

   _____

10. You listen with your eyes.

    _____

Copyright © 1997 by Academic Communication Associates. This form may be reproduced.

11. He winked his ear.

_____

12. Sally ate a shoe.

_____

13. The book fell up.

_____

14. Barry drove his sandwich to the zoo.

_____

15. Timmy went swimming in the puddle.

_____

16. Mary baked cookies in the garage.

_____

17. Lisa sliced the lemons with a bat.

_____

18. Carl ate sausage and footballs for breakfast.

_____

19. Lyle spread butter on his pencil.

_____

20. Mom gave her baby a rattlesnake.

_____

ACTIVITY 3 - SILLY SENTENCES

Name:_____ Date:_____

Instructions: The following sentences contain absurdities. Have the child fix each silly sentence after you read it to him or her.

1. Barry dried himself off with a napkin.

   _____

2. Mr. Gabler put cream and salt in his coffee.

   _____

3. Amy put pepper in her cookies.

   _____

4. Leslie put her coat on to go swimming.

   _____

5. Mike put his hat on his foot.

   _____

6. Barbara always sat on a telephone.

   _____

7. Doug ironed his pants with a rock.

   _____

8. Linda ate paper chips for a snack.

   _____

9. Bill listened to the lights in the car.

   _____

10. Peggy cleaned the floor with tar.

   _____

Copyright © 1997 by Academic Communication Associates. This form may be reproduced.

11. Tommy ate spaghetti and tennis balls for lunch.

_____

12. Rita played the knife and fork.

_____

13. Billy skated on his tennis shoes.

_____

14. Patty washed her hair with dirt.

_____

15. Cal used a brush to sweep the floors.

_____

16. Maria fixed the pipe with a piece of bubble gum.

_____

17. Freddie ate peanut butter on his steak.

_____

18. Leslie paid for her dress with a banana.

_____

19. Ned fed the cows a bale of plastic.

_____

20. Mrs. Greenberg told her son to wear his pots and pans.

_____

ACTIVITY 4 - ANSWERING QUESTIONS ABOUT SENTENCES

Name:_____ Date:_____

Instructions: The child is asked to respond to questions related to the content of a sentence presented orally by the teacher. Read each sentence and ask the question that follows.

___ 1. Donna is looking at her book.

     Is Donna reading or watching television?

___ 2. Lupe's bird sleeps in the morning.

     Is Lupe's bird awake or asleep in the morning?

___ 3. Karen is drinking a cold glass of soda.

     Is Karen hungry or thirsty?

___ 4. Lisa's toy is shaped like a ball.

     Is Lisa's toy round or square?

___ 5. Tim's hat is the same color as the sun.

     Is the hat blue or yellow?

___ 6. The painting is above the refrigerator.

     Is the painting low or high?

___ 7. Tina's mouse is smaller than her rabbit.

     Is Tina's rabbit her smallest animal?

___ 8. The road is very bumpy.

     Is the road smooth or rough?

___ 9. The snow is falling from the sky.

     Is it a hot day or a cold day?

___10. The children were very noisy.

     Were the children quiet or loud?

___11. Lisa traveled on a boat.

     Did Lisa travel by sea or air?

___12. Mary has a pet with four legs that barks.

     Does Mary have a pet dog or a pet bird?

Copyright © 1997 by Academic Communication Associates. This form may be reproduced.

___13. It is hard to see in the room.

    Is it light or dark?

___14. The parents named the baby, Cathy.

    Is the baby a boy or a girl?

___15. The Fishers have twins.

    Do the Fisher's have one child or two?

___16. Christopher likes the color of pumpkins.

    Does Christopher like red or orange?

___17. Mr. Sanders uses a vehicle with four wheels to get to work.

    Does Mr. Sanders ride a bicycle or drive a car to work?

___18. Sally's favorite food is red and has black seeds inside.

    Does Sally like lemons or watermelon?

___19. Brandy is five years old.

    Is Brandy's older sister six or four?

___20. Jack builds houses.

    Is Jack an astronaut or a carpenter?

___21. Linda is a doctor.

    Does Linda take care of people or gardens?

___22. The weather is very hot.

    Should Linda wear a coat or a pair of shorts?

___23. Billy likes to eat sweet things for dessert.

    Does Billy like to eat cookies or pickles for dessert?

___24. Mindy is a monkey.

    Do you think Mindy likes steak or bananas?

___25. Buddy is at the playground.

    Is Buddy inside or outside?

___26. Mrs. Chapman is teaching math.

    Are Mrs. Chapman's students learning about numbers or letters?

___27. Laura rides a bicycle every morning.

    Does Laura pedal or does she row?

___28. Casey mailed a package.

    Did Casey go to the post office or to a bank?

___29. The sun is going down.

    Is it morning or evening?

___30. Tyler doesn't eat any meat.

Does Tyler eat vegetables or ham?

___31. The cat is striped.

Does the cat have lines or circles on it?

___32. Wendy is wearing a red dress.

Is Wendy's dress the color of apples or oranges?

___33. Ben is wearing a hat.

Is Ben wearing something on his head or on his shoulders?

___34. The family eats a big meal for breakfast.

Does the family eat a big meal in the morning or at night?

___35. Tammy is wearing a bracelet.

Is Tammy wearing something around her wrist or around her neck?

ACTIVITY 5 - COMPLETE THE SENTENCE

Name:_____ Date:_____

Instructions: The child's task is to complete each sentence by changing the final word to another word that makes sense.

1. Clean the kitchen with a broom.

    Clean the kitchen with a _____

2. It is time to go for a swim.

    It is time to go for a_____

3. The cat jumped over the gate.

    The cat jumped over the _____.

4. The teacher came into the restaurant.

    The teacher came into the _____.

5. Put the pencil in the yellow box.

    Put the pencil in the yellow _____.

6. Sarah came to school without her lunch.

    Sarah came to school without her _____.

7. Paul went into his room to get a book.

    Paul went into his room to get a _____.

8. William was happy because it was time to eat.

    William was happy because it was time to _____.

9. Carol put her new shoes in the closet.

    Carol put her new shoes in the _____.

10. The dog took the pillow off the bed.

    The dog took the pillow off the _____.

11. The book fell off the table.

    The book fell off the _____.

12. Listen to the man who is talking.

    Listen to the man who is _____.

13. Christopher is drawing a picture of a house.

    Christopher is drawing a picture of a _____.

Copyright © 1997 by Academic Communication Associates. This form may be reproduced.

14. Sam is putting a new rug in the office.

    Sam is putting a new rug in the _____.

15. The weather was cool at the beach.

    The weather was cool at the _____.

16. The store closed late at night.

    The store closed late at _____.

17. Sarah drove her car into the garage.

    Sarah drove her car into the _____.

18. The waiter dropped the water on the carpet.

    The waiter dropped the water on the _____.

19. It was very hot when Carol turned on the fan.

    It was very hot when Carol turned on the _____.

20. Before the party, Christopher shined his shoes.

    Before the party, Christopher shined his _____.

ACTIVITY 6 - FIX THE SENTENCE

Name:_____ Date:_____

Instructions: A sentence is read to the child that makes no sense. The sentence is then read a second time with the final word missing. The child's task is to change the last word to a word that makes sense within the sentence.

> *Example*: Ricky was thirsty so he drank a glass of sand.
>
> Ricky was thirsty so he drank a glass of _____.
>
> *Sample response*: water

1. Ricky was hungry so he ate a piece of wood.

   Ricky was hungry so he ate a piece of _____.

2. Sarah put her sock on her elbow.

   Sarah put her sock on her _____.

3. Andy wrote a letter with a candle.

   Andy wrote a letter with a _____.

4. Carla listened to music on the fan.

   Carla listen to music on the _____.

5. The teacher was reading a spider.

   The teacher was reading a _____

6. The beehive had lots of horses.

   The beehive had lots of _____.

7. Kelly wore her new telephone.

   Kelly wore her new _____.

8. Mark used a key to unlock the banana.

   Mark used a key to unlock the _____.

Copyright © 1997 by Academic Communication Associates. This form may be reproduced.

9. Sandy drank some toothpicks.

   Sandy drank some _____.

10. Beverly rode to school on her broom.

    Beverly rode to school on her _____.

11. Mrs. Smith planted some pretty plates.

    Mrs. Smith planted some pretty _____.

12. Dan hit the baseball with a balloon.

    Dan hit the baseball with a _____.

13. Ron put the milk carton in the mailbox.

    Ron put the milk carton in the _____.

14. Peter drove his car down the elephant.

    Peter drove his car down the _____.

15. Mr. Smith played pretty music with his dishwasher.

    Mr. Smith played pretty music with his _____.

16. Jenni washed her shirt in the telescope.

    Jenni washed her shirt in the _____.

17. Chuck slept on his vacuum cleaner.

    Chuck slept on his _____.

18. Sarah was cold so she put on a heavy snowball.

    Sarah was cold so she put on a heavy _____.

ACTIVITY 7 - COMPARISON QUESTIONS

Name: _____   Date:_____

Instructions: The child's task is to answer each question by comparing two nouns.

___ 1. Is an elephant lighter than a shoe?

___ 2. Is a spoon sharper than a knife?

___ 3. Is a puppy friendlier than a lion?

___ 4. Is a sock softer than a rock?

___ 5. Is a whisper louder than a shout?

___ 6. Is a baby older than a teenager?

___ 7. Is a giraffe shorter than a mouse?

___ 8. Is a flame hotter than an ice cube?

___ 9. Is an elephant stronger than a grasshopper?

___10. Is an onion sweeter than chocolate?

___11. Is a bike longer than an airplane?

___12. Is a snail faster than a cat?

___13. Is a peanut crunchier than a tomato?

___14. Is a year shorter than a day?

___15. Is wood harder than rubber?

___16. Is a pig skinnier than a lizard?

___17. Is a feather heavier than a washing machine?

___18. Is an apple thicker than a cherry?

___19. Is a siren softer than a cat?

___20. Is a worm longer than a snake?

Copyright © 1997 by Academic Communication Associates. This form may be reproduced.

ACTIVITY 8 - THINK OF A WORD

Name: _____   Date:_____

Instructions: The child's task is to complete each sentence by naming an appropriate noun.

1. A car is heavier than a _____

2. A spider is smaller than a _____

3. A lion is stronger than a _____

4. A man is taller than a _____

5. A watermelon is thicker than a _____

6. A trumpet is louder than a _____

7. A lake is bigger than a _____

8. A sponge is softer than a _____

9. An airplane is faster than a _____

10. A worm is thinner than a _____

11. An oven is hotter than a _____

12. A pencil is smoother than a _____

13. A building is larger than a _____

14. A turtle is slower than a _____

15. Candy is sweeter than _____

16. A bike is smaller than a _____

17. Night is darker than _____

18. A rock is harder than a _____

ACTIVITY 9 - LABELING NOUNS BY ATTRIBUTES

Name: _____   Date:_____

Instructions: The child's task is to name nouns that have specific attributes.

1. Name a number that is bigger than one.   _____
2. Name a tool that has a blade.   _____
3. Name something that has a heel.   _____
4. Name something that you can bend.   _____
5. Name something that you can see through.   _____
6. Name something that can be sprayed.   _____
7. Name something that has a lid.   _____
8. Name something that needs gas.   _____
9. Name something that is cold.   _____
10. Name something that is square.   _____
11. Name something that has a handle.   _____
12. Name something that is used under water.   _____
13. Name something that has frosting.   _____
14. Name something that smells sweet.   _____
15. Name something that is red.   _____
16. Name something that grows on a tree.   _____
17. Name something that has more than two wheels.   _____
18. Name something that has a switch.   _____
19. Name something that is used to clean.   _____
20. Name something tiny that crawls.   _____
21. Name something red that is round.   _____
22. Name something yellow that has a peel.   _____
23. Name something sharp that has a handle.   _____
24. Name something round that is flat.   _____
25. Name something that grows under the ground.   _____

Copyright © 1997 by Academic Communication Associates. This form may be reproduced.

ACTIVITY IO - NAMING OBJECTS BY LOCATION

Name: _____   Date: _____

Instructions: The child's task is to name objects associated with specific situations.

 1. Name something you would see on a playground.   _____

 2. Name something you would see in the jungle.   _____

 3. Name something you would see at the beach.   _____

 4. Name something you would use in your kitchen at home. _____

 5. Name something you would turn on in the bathroom at home. _____

 6. Name something that you would see in a garage.   _____

 7. Name something you would put in a refrigerator.   _____

 8. Name something you would see in the supermarket.   _____

 9. Name something you would see in the park.   _____

10. Name something you would see at a baseball game.   _____

11. Name something you would see at a doctor's office.   _____

12. Name something you would use at the laundromat.   _____

13. Name something you would take to the post office.   _____

14. Name something you would buy at a hardware store.   _____

15. Name something you would see at a movie theater.   _____

16. Name something you would pick up at a cafeteria.   _____

17. Name something you would look at in the library.   _____

18. Name something you would use in an office.   _____

19. Name something you would use in a classroom.   _____

20. Name something you would buy in a bakery.   _____

Copyright © 1997 by Academic Communication Associates. This form may be reproduced.

ACTIVITY II - NOUN FUNCTIONS

Name: _____   Date:_____

Instructions: The child's task is to describe the function of each noun.

1. I'm a knife. You use me to _____.

2. I'm a cup. You use me to _____.

3. I'm a ball. You use me to _____.

4. I'm a pair of glasses. You use me to _____.

5. I'm a hat. You use me to _____.

6. I'm a bat. You use me to _____.

7. I'm a bed. You use me to _____.

8. I'm a television set. You use me to _____.

9. I'm a coat. You use me to _____.

10. I'm a chair. You use me to _____.

11. I'm an eraser. You use me to _____.

12. I'm a crayon. You use me to _____.

13. I'm a toothbrush. You use me to _____.

14. I'm a radio. You use me to _____.

15. I'm a car. You use me to _____.

16. I'm a wallet. You use me to _____.

17. I'm a stamp. You use me to _____.

18. I'm a dollar bill. You use me to _____.

19. I'm a closet. You use me to _____.

Copyright © 1997 by Academic Communication Associates. This form may be reproduced.

20. I'm a playground. You use me to _____.

21. I'm a computer. You use me to _____.

22. I'm an oven. You use me to _____.

23. I'm a boat. You use me to _____.

24. I'm a bathtub. You use me to _____.

25. I'm a lawn mower. You use me to _____.

26. I'm a piece of tape. You use me to _____.

27. I'm sunglasses. You use me to _____.

28. I'm a vacuum cleaner. You use me to _____.

29. I'm a golf club. You use me to _____.

30. I'm a fan. You use me to _____.

ACTIVITY 12 - IDENTIFYING WORDS FROM DESCRIPTIONS

Name: _____ Date:_____

Instructions: A description of a word is read to the student. The student's task is to identify the word that was described.

1. I am round and bounce. What am I? _____

2. You write with me. I have an eraser. What am I? _____

3. You drink me. I am white and come from a cow. What am I? _____

4. I have four wheels and take you for a ride. What am I? _____

5. I have laces and go on your foot. What am I? _____

6. You open me before walking into your house. What am I? _____

7. You wear me over your shirt when it is cold. What am I? _____

8. You use me to cut your food. What am I? _____

9. You read me in class. What am I? _____

10. I tick. You use me to find out what time it is. What am I? _____

11. You sleep on me at night. What am I? _____

12. You use me when the room is too dark? What am I? _____

13. You put food inside me when you are shopping. What am I? _____

14. I have a motor, wings, and I fly through the sky. What am I? _____

15. I spin fast and cool off the room on a hot day. What am I? _____

16. You put toothpaste on me before brushing. What am I? _____

17. You lick me and put me on an envelope. What am I? _____

18. I have five toes and you cover me with a sock. What am I? _____

19. You watch programs and commercials on me. What am I? _____

20. You wear me on your head. What am I? _____

Copyright © 1997 by Academic Communication Associates. This form may be reproduced.

ACTIVITY 13 - NAME THE ANIMAL

Name: _____   Date:_____

Instructions: The child is asked to identify the animal described in each item below.

1. I have four legs and bark.   _____

2. I have wings and live in a nest.   _____

3. I have spots and a very long neck.   _____

4. I have a long trunk.   _____

5. I say "meow."   _____

6. I have a white stripe and I smell bad.   _____

7. I eat a lot and say "oink."   _____

8. I have fins and swim in the water.   _____

9. I'm long and crawl on the ground.   _____

10. I hop and I have a pouch.   _____

11. I live on a farm and lay eggs.   _____

12. I say "moo." Milk comes from me.   _____

13. Cowboys like to ride me.   _____

14. I like to eat cheese. Cats like to chase me. _____

15. I love to eat bananas.   _____

16. People eat me on Thanksgiving.   _____

Copyright © 1997 by Academic Communication Associates. This form may be reproduced.

ACTIVITY 14 - WHICH ONE DOESN'T BELONG?

Name: _____   Date:_____

Instructions: The child's task is to choose the item that does not belong with a specific item. Circle the child's response.

1. Which one doesn't belong with apple?   cherry, pear, sock
2. Which one doesn't belong with penny?   dollar, spoon, dime
3. Which one doesn't belong with brother?   sister, father, cow
4. Which one doesn't belong with hammer?   screwdriver, bed, saw
5. Which one doesn't belong with book?   bandage, newspaper, magazine
6. Which one doesn't belong with happy?   glad, sad, cheerful
7. Which one doesn't belong with shirt?   coat, television, pants
8. Which one doesn't belong with car?   lamp, truck, van
9. Which one doesn't belong with cake?   pie, cookie, onion
10. Which one doesn't belong with fork?   spoon, wallet, knife
11. Which one doesn't belong with summer?   winter, Wednesday, autumn
12. Which one doesn't belong with football?   tennis, basketball, shopping
13. Which one doesn't belong with seven?   telephone, nine, four
14. Which one doesn't belong with horse?   cow, butterfly, donkey
15. Which one doesn't belong with house?   apartment, hotel, desert
16. Which one doesn't belong with pencil?   crayon, pen, scissors
17. Which one doesn't belong with soap?   detergent, lemonade, shampoo
18. Which one doesn't belong with chair?   suitcase, bed, table
19. Which one doesn't belong with red?   green, square, blue
20. Which one doesn't belong with flower?   plant, vine, pole
21. Which one doesn't go with leg?   arm, wood, foot
22. Which word doesn't go with piano?   guitar, lamp, flute
23. Which word doesn't go with boy?   man, girl, rooster
24. Which word doesn't go with shark?   dolphin, tree, whale

Copyright © 1997 by Academic Communication Associates. This form may be reproduced.

ACTIVITY 15 - ITEMS WITHIN CATEGORIES

Name: _____   Date:_____

Instructions: The child's task is to name nouns that fit within specific categories.

1. A penny is a coin. Name another coin. _____

2. Monday is a day of the week. Name another day of the week. _____

3. A shirt is a type of clothing. Name something else that is clothing. _____

4. A chair is a type of furniture. Name something else that is furniture. _____

5. A house is a building. Name another building. _____

6. A hammer is a tool. Name another tool. _____

7. Red is a color. Name another color. _____

8. Los Angeles is a city. Name another city. _____

9. Macaroni is a food. Name another food. _____

10. A lion is a jungle animal. Name another jungle animal. _____

11. A ring is a type of jewelry. Name something else that is jewelry. _____

12. A guitar is a musical instrument. Name another musical instrument. _____

13. An apple is a fruit. Name another fruit. _____

14. Mars is a planet. Name another planet. _____

15. A parrot is a bird. Name another bird. _____

16. A square is a shape. Name another shape. _____

17. A toaster is an electric appliance. Name another electric appliance. _____

18. A truck is a motor vehicle. Name another motor vehicle. _____

19. Celery is a vegetable. Name another vegetable. _____

20. Baseball is a sport. Name another sport. _____

21. Winter is a season. Name another season. _____

22. A box is a container. Name another kind of container. _____

Copyright © 1997 by Academic Communication Associates. This form may be reproduced.

ACTIVITY 16 - COMPLETING ANALOGIES

Name: _____   Date:_____

Instructions: The child's task is to complete each sentence by using the appropriate word.

1. A giant is large. A baby is _____.

2. A car is heavy. A pencil is _____.

3. A snail is slow. A dog is _____.

4. A hero is brave. A coward is _____.

5. A witch is ugly. A princess is _____.

6. A rock is hard. A sponge is _____.

7. The evening is dark. The morning is _____.

8. A carrot is good to eat. Milk is good to _____.

9. The bottom is down. The top is _____.

10. A boy who laughs is happy. A boy who cries is _____.

11. Raisins are black. Snow is _____.

12. Candy is sweet. Pickles are _____.

13. Summer is hot. Winter is _____.

14. Christopher is a boy. Linda is a _____.

15. The quiet girl whispers. The noisy girl _____.

16. A man has a house. A bird has a _____.

17. February is a month. Monday is a _____.

18. A scream is loud. A whisper is _____.

19. A baby is young. A grandfather is _____.

20. The ceiling is high. The floor is _____.

21. A pet is tame. A lion is _____.

22. Fresh food is good. Stale food is _____.

23. A friend is nice. An enemy is _____.

Copyright © 1997 by Academic Communication Associates. This form may be reproduced.

ACTIVITY 17 - FOLLOWING DIRECTIONS   (WORKSHEET A)

Name:_____ Date:_____

Materials: Picture Worksheet A in Appendix A

Instructions: The child's task is to follow the teacher's instructions for completing the worksheet. Record a plus (+) for correct responses and a minus (–) for incorrect responses.

> *Say*: "Look at the rows of pictures. Each row has four pictures of items in it. I want you to listen carefully and to do what I tell you to do."

Top Row

___1. Circle the item that covers your legs.

___2. Color the item that covers your chest and arms.

___3. Put a square around something that you might have as a pet.

___4. Mark an X over the animal that has cubs.

Middle Row

___1. Mark an X over the item that gets very hot and is used to get rid of wrinkles.

___2. Color the item that is used in the morning to make toast.

___3. Circle the item that you sit on at the dinner table.

___4. Draw a picture of yourself sitting on the piece of furniture that belongs in the living room.

Bottom Row

___1. Color the item without laces that goes on your foot.

___2. Circle the item with laces that you wear to protect your foot.

___3. Draw a feather in the item that you wear on your head.

___4. Point to the thing that you wear to keep your ears warm.

Copyright © 1997 by Academic Communication Associates. This form may be reproduced.

ACTIVITY 17 - FOLLOWING DIRECTIONS   (WORKSHEET B)

Name:_____ Date:_____

Materials: Picture Worksheet B in Appendix A

Instructions: The child's task is to follow the teacher's instructions for completing the worksheet. Record a plus (+) for correct responses and a minus (–) for incorrect responses.

Say: "Look at the rows of pictures. Each row has four pictures of items in it. I want you to listen carefully and to do what I tell you to do."

Top Row

___1. Draw some potatoes in the thing that you put on the stove.

___2. Color the insect that has a hard outer shell.

___3. Mark an X over the insect that flies and makes honey.

___4. Color the item that is used to stir things.

Middle Row

___1. Circle the item that is used to tie down a large load.

___2. Mark an X over the item that is hooked up to a trailer.

___3. Color the piece of jewelry that is worn around the neck.

___4. Point to the item that is worn on the finger.

Bottom Row

___1. Color the item that makes a ringing sound.

___2. Circle the item that you can use to draw.

___3. Point to the item that you blow to make a sound.

___4. Draw a square next to the item that you use to write.

Copyright © 1997 by Academic Communication Associates. This form may be reproduced.

ACTIVITY 17 - FOLLOWING DIRECTIONS   (WORKSHEET C)

Name:_____ Date:_____

Materials: Picture Worksheet C in Appendix A

Instructions: The child's task is to follow the teacher's instructions for completing the worksheet. Record a plus (+) for correct responses and a minus (–) for incorrect responses.

Say: "Look at the rows of pictures. Each row has four pictures of items in it. I want you to listen carefully and to do what I tell you to do."

Top Row

___1. Circle the animal that roars and lives in Africa.

___2. Draw a red line under the animal that growls and likes to eat honey.

___3. Color the animal that has four legs and sheds its skin.

___4. Circle the animal that crawls on its belly?

Middle Row

___1. Circle the crunchy fruit that is red.

___2. Color the light green vegetable that grows in stalks.

___3. Point to the fruit that is smaller on top than it is on the bottom.

___4. Mark an X over the orange vegetable that is loved by rabbits.

Bottom Row

___1. Circle the food that has pepperoni and cheese on it.

___2. Color the fruit that looks like a bunch of little marbles.

___3. Mark an X over the fruit that is the same color as a lemon.

___4. Point to the food that goes well with french fries and ketchup.

Copyright © 1997 by Academic Communication Associates. This form may be reproduced.

ACTIVITY 17 - FOLLOWING DIRECTIONS (WORKSHEET D)

Name:_____ Date:_____

Materials: Picture Worksheet D in Appendix A

Instructions: The child's task is to follow the teacher's instructions for completing the worksheet. Record a plus (+) for correct responses and a minus (–) for incorrect responses.

Say: "Look at the rows of pictures. Each row has four pictures of items in it. I want you to listen carefully and to do what I tell you to do."

Top Row:

___1. Color the item that has four wheels and is used for transportation.

___2. Draw a bell on the item that has two wheels and is pedaled.

___3. Circle the item that travels through the air.

___4. Mark an X over the item that travels on water.

Middle Row:

___1. Color the animal that has stripes and four legs.

___2. Draw a circle around the animal that neighs and gallops.

___3. Mark an X over the animal that "oinks" and rolls around in the mud.

___4. Point to the animal that climbs trees and loves to eat bananas.

Bottom Row:

___1. Circle the item that looks like a circle.

___2. Color the item that is square and used to store things.

___3. Mark an X over the item that holds peanut butter.

___4. Draw a line through the item that is a square toy.

Copyright © 1997 by Academic Communication Associates. This form may be reproduced.

ACTIVITY 17 - FOLLOWING DIRECTIONS   (WORKSHEET E)

Name:_____ Date:_____

Materials: Picture Worksheet E in Appendix A

Instructions: The child's task is to follow the teacher's instructions for completing the worksheet. Record a plus (+) for correct responses and a minus (–) for incorrect responses.

Say: "Look at the rows of pictures. Each row has four pictures of items in it. I want you to listen carefully and to do what I tell you to do."

Top Row:

___1. Color the item that hangs on the wall and tells you what time it is.

___2. Circle the item that is worn on the wrist and used to tell time.

___3. Mark an X over the item that is read, has pages, and sometimes has a hard cover.

___4. Draw a line through the item that people read to find out the news.

Middle Row:

___1. Point to the item that is used to hit a ball over a net.

___2. Color the item that is used to pick up food to eat.

___3. Circle the item that is used to cut meat.

___4. Mark an X over the item that is used to hit a baseball.

Bottom Row:

___1. Color the animal that has eight legs.

___2. Circle the animal that barks and likes to be taken for walks.

___3. Point to the animal that has fins and swims.

___4. Draw a line through the animal that meows and scratches things.

Copyright © 1997 by Academic Communication Associates. This form may be reproduced.

ACTIVITY 18 - DO WHAT I SAY

Materials: Reproduce the pictures on the following page. Cut out each character's picture for use in this activity.

Instructions: A picture of a character is presented and the child is told to respond to verbal commands only when they are preceded by the name of this character. The instructions for the first set of commands should be presented as follows:

> "Here is a picture of Rusty Raccoon. He will ask you to do some things. Do what he tells you to do. If Mary Mouse or another animal tells you to do something, don't do anything at all. Do only what Rusty Raccoon says to do."

Four sets of verbal commands are included in this activity:

Set A: The child is to respond only to commands preceded by the words, "Rusty says." (Stimulus Picture: Rusty Raccoon)

Set B: The child is to respond only to commands preceded by the words, "Jason says." (Stimulus Picture: Jason the Bear)

Set C: The child is to respond only to commands preceded by the words, "Mary says." (Stimulus Picture: Mary Mouse)

Set D: The child is to respond only to commands preceded by the words, "Robbie says." (Stimulus Picture: Robbie Rabbit)

Character Pictures

These pictures are needed for Activity 18. They may also be used with other activities that include these characters.

Rusty Raccoon

Jason the Bear

Mary Mouse

Robbie Rabbit

Copyright © 1997 by Academic Communication Associates. These pictures may be reproduced.

Name:_____ Date:_____

Activity 18 - Set A
Rusty Raccoon

Say: "Listen to these instructions. Do only what Rusty Raccoon tells you to do."

___ 1. Rusty says, "Sit down."

___ 2. Rusty says, "Touch your nose."

___ 3. Mary Mouse says, "Put your hand over your mouth."

___ 4. Rusty says, "Turn around."

___ 5. Rusty says, "Wave good-bye."

___ 6. Rodney Rabbit says, "Jump twice."

___ 7. Rusty says, "Rub your tummy."

___ 8. Rusty says, "Raise your arms."

___ 9. Mary Mouse says, "Touch your ears."

___10. Rusty says, "Jump one time."

___11. Rusty says, "Touch your knee."

___12. Rusty says, "Wink your eye."

___13. Rusty says, "Touch your elbow."

___14. Ella Elephant says, "Eat a peanut."

___15. Rusty says, "Touch the ground."

___16. Rusty says, "Touch your hair."

___17. Rusty says, "Touch your ear."

___18. Leo the Lion says, "Smile."

___19. Rusty says, "Pat your friend's back."

___20. Rusty says, "Jump three times."

Copyright © 1997 by Academic Communication Associates. This form may be reproduced.

Name:_____ Date:_____

Activity 18 - Set B
Jason the Bear

Say: "Now Jason the Bear is in charge of giving all instructions. Follow only instructions from Jason."

___ 1. Jason says, "Touch your elbow, then touch your nose."

___ 2. Jason says, "Touch your hair, then touch your ear."

___ 3. Jason says, "Turn around once, then sit down."

___ 4. Jake the Snake says, "Hiss, then blow a kiss."

___ 5. Jason says, "Count to two, then hold up two fingers."

___ 6. Jason says, "Close your eyes, then touch your head."

___ 7. Mary Mouse says, "Look at your feet, then yawn."

___ 8. Jason says, "Put your head down, then clap your hands."

___ 9. Jason says, "Touch your toes, then raise your hand."

___10. Jerry says, "Bark like a dog, then stomp your foot."

___11. Jason says, "Meow like a cat, then lick your lips."

___12. Jasmine says, "Shake your head, then stretch."

___13. Jason says, "Shake your leg, then flap your arms."

___14. Jason says, "Jump once, then sit down."

___15. Larry Lizard says, "Stick out your tongue, then whistle."

___16. Jason says, "Wiggle your fingers, then touch your nose."

___17. Jason says, "Tap your foot, then count to four."

___18. Jason says, "Smack your lips, then walk to the door."

___19. Jack says, "Scratch your head, then clap your hands."

___20. Jason says, "Nod your head, then smack your lips."

Copyright © 1997 by Academic Communication Associates. This form may be reproduced.

Name:_____ Date:_____

Activity 18 - Set C
Mary Mouse

Say: "Now Mary Mouse is in charge of giving instructions. Do only what Mary Mouse tells you to do."

___ 1. Mary says, "Tap your foot, close your eyes, then rub your stomach."

___ 2. Mary says, "Scratch your knee, touch your neck, then clap your hands."

___ 3. Mindy says, "Cover your mouth, clap your hands, then jump one time."

___ 4. Mary says, "Cross your legs, cross your fingers, then shake your body."

___ 5. Mary says, "Count to five, raise two fingers, then look down at the floor."

___ 6. Manny Monkey says, "Touch your nose, take a deep breath, then jump.

___ 7. Mary says, "Stretch your arms, sit down, then open your mouth."

___ 8. Mary says, "Raise your leg, touch the floor, then squat."

___ 9. Mindy says, "Close your eyes, stomp your foot, then touch your ear."

___10. Mary says, "Touch your shoulder, twitch your nose, then bend over."

___11. Mary says, "Shuffle your feet, laugh out loud, then rub your tummy."

___12. Mary says, "Lick your lips, pat your stomach, then touch your nose."

___13. Mary says, "Cover your ears, bend your arm, then cross your fingers."

___14. Manny says, "Shuffle your feet, rub your elbows, then raise your hand."

___15. Mary says, "Touch your nose, touch your ears, then bend your legs."

___16. Mary says, "March in place, blink, then blow a kiss."

___17. Mindy says, "Twitch your nose, touch your ear, then pat your head."

___18. Mary says, "Pat your knee, smile, then clap your hands."

___19. Mary says, "Rub your neck, pinch your arm, then raise one hand.

___20. Mindy says, "Open your mouth, pat your cheeks, then slap your thighs."

Copyright © 1997 by Academic Communication Associates. This form may be reproduced.

Name:_____ Date:_____

Activity 18 - Set D
Robbie Rabbit

Say: "Robbie Rabbit is now in charge of giving instructions. Do only what Robbie Rabbit tells you to do."

___ 1. Robbie says, "Act like a chicken."

___ 2. Rodney Rat says, "Act like a monkey."

___ 3. Robbie says, "Moo like a cow."

___ 4. Robbie says, "Neigh like a horse."

___ 5. Robbie says, "Flap your arms like a bird."

___ 6. Randy says, "Jump like a frog."

___ 7. Robbie says, "Stretch your arms out like a tall giraffe."

___ 8. Robbie says, "Roll your eyes like a lizard."

___ 9. Randy says, "Swim like a fish through the air."

___10. Robbie says, "Roar like a lion."

___11. Robbie says, "Growl like an alligator."

___12. Robbie says, "Sing like a bird."

___13. Rodney Rat says, "Laugh like a hyena."

___14. Robbie says, "Crow like a rooster."

___15. Robbie says, "Oink like a pig."

___16. Robbie says, "Croak like a frog."

___17. Randy says, "Jump like a kangaroo."

___18. Robbie says, "Squawk like a parrot."

___19. Robbie says, "Screech like an owl."

___20. Randy says, "Gobble like a turkey."

Copyright © 1997 by Academic Communication Associates. This form may be reproduced.

ACTIVITY 19 - LISTENING FOR ERRORS

Name:_____ Date:_____

Instructions: The child is presented with descriptions of situations in which Jason the Bear is asked to respond to verbal commands. The child's task is to identify errors made by Jason in following these commands.

Say: "Jason the Bear is not listening very carefully today. Listen to the things that his mother asked him to do and tell me what he did wrong."

1. "Please brush your hair and close the door," said Mother.

   Jason brushed his teeth and closed the door. Did he do the right thing?

   _____

2. "Please wash the dishes and sweep the floor," said Mother.

   Jason swept the floor and washed the windows. Did he do the right thing?

   _____

3. "Please turn on the radio and bring me the mop," said Mother.

   Jason brought her the mop and turned on the television. Did he do the right thing?

   _____

4. "Please feed the cat and clean your room," said Mother.

   Jason cleaned his room and fed the bird. Did he do the right thing?

   _____

5. "Please put the plates on the table and put the milk in the refrigerator," said Mother.

   Jason put the plates in the refrigerator and put the milk on the table. Did he do the right thing?

   _____

6. "Please sit in the small chair and put the box under the table," said Mother.

   Jason sat in the small chair and put the box on top of the table. Did he do the right thing?

   _____

Copyright © 1997 by Academic Communication Associates. This form may be reproduced.

7. "Please put your coat in the closet and put the pillow on the couch," said Mother.

    Jason put his hat in the closet and put the pillow on the couch. Did he do the right thing?

    _____

8. "Please wash the cups and put the spoons in the drawer," said Mother.

    Jason washed the spoons and put the cups in the drawer. Did he do the right thing?

    _____

9. "Please turn on the light in the kitchen and put the soap in the box," said Mother.

    Jason turned on the light and put the box near the soap. Did he do the right thing?

    _____

10. "Please close the curtain and put the broom by the door," said Mother.

    Jason closed the curtain and put the chair by the door. Did he do the right thing?

    _____

11. "Please rake the leaves and put the rocks in a box," said Mother.

    Jason put the rake in a box and put the leaves near the rocks. Did he do the right thing?

    _____

12. "Please put your book in the bookcase and put your shirt in the drawer," said Mother.

    Jason put his pants in the drawer and put the book in the bookcase. Did he do the right thing?

    _____

13. "Please put the letter in the envelope and sweep the porch," said Mother.

    Jason put the envelope in a box and swept the porch. Did he do the right thing?

    _____

14. "Please close the door to the garage and put the tools in the yard," said Mother.

    Jason put the tools in the yard and closed the door to the house. Did he do the right thing?

    _____

ACTIVITY 20 - GIVING ORAL DIRECTIONS

Name:_____ Date:_____

Materials: Pictures of Jason the Bear and Mary Mouse on page 41.

Instructions: Place the pictures of Jason the Bear and Mary Mouse in front of the child. Ask the child to give the following oral instructions. The child should use the animal character's name when responding.

> *Example*: Tell Jason the Bear to write his name on the paper.
> *Sample response*: Write your name on the paper, Jason.

___ 1. Tell Jason to write his name on his paper.

___ 2. Tell Jason to sit down and read his book.

___ 3. Tell Jason to walk to the door and open it.

___ 4. Tell Jason to brush his teeth and wash his face.

___ 5. Tell Mary Mouse to fold the paper and write her name on it.

___ 6. Tell Jason the Bear to stand near the door until he hears the bell.

___ 7. Tell Mary Mouse to write her name on the paper and to draw a picture.

___ 8. Tell Mary Mouse to put a red crayon and a blue crayon in the box.

___ 9. Tell Jason to put his coat on the hook that is near the door.

___10. Tell Mary Mouse to turn the light on and to open the door.

___11. Tell Jason to sharpen the pencils and to put them near the window.

___12. Tell Jason to plug in the fan and to turn on the television.

___13. Tell Mary Mouse to pick up a piece of chalk and put it in an envelope.

___14. Tell Jason to draw a square on a piece of paper and to color it red.

___15. Tell Mary Mouse to put on her coat and to stand near the window.

___16. Tell Jason to open a book and to turn to the first page.

Copyright © 1997 by Academic Communication Associates. This form may be reproduced.

ACTIVITY 21 - IDENTIFYING MISSING INFORMATION

Name:_____ Date:_____

Instructions: The child is presented with descriptions of situations in which a character needs to remember three things. The child's task is to state what the character forgot.

1. Kim needed to buy a banana, apple, and pear at the store. When she got home from the store, she had a banana and a pear. What did she forget?

   _____

2. Mother asked Roger to wash the car, cut the grass, and paint the fence. Roger painted the fence and cut the grass. What did he forget to do? _____

3. Sam asked Mary to buy a shirt, tie, and coat. Mary went to the store and bought a shirt and a coat. What did she forget to buy? _____

4. The teacher asked Tom to find crayons that were blue, green, and red. Tom found crayons that were green and red. What color did he forget? _____

5. The teacher asked Randy for the pencil, the book, and the box. Randy handed the teacher the pencil and the book. What did he forget? _____

6. Sam asked Ron for a penny, dime, and quarter. Ron handed Sam a quarter and a dime. What did he forget? _____

7. Carl asked John to buy bread, soda, and milk at the store. John bought soda and bread. What did he forget? _____

8. Peter asked Linda to order cake, pizza, and cheese for the party. Linda bought pizza and cake for the party. What did she forget? _____

9. Carol asked Donna to buy cereal, spaghetti, and rice at the store. Donna bought rice and cereal. What did she forget? _____

10. Linda asked Marty to go to the supermarket, bank, and the library. Linda went to the bank and supermarket. Where did she forget to go? _____

11. Sarah was asked to call Tom, Andy, and Lisa. Sarah called Tom and Lisa. Who did she forget to call? _____

Copyright © 1997 by Academic Communication Associates. This form may be reproduced.

12. Betty asked Ellen to put forks, napkins, and potato chips on the table. Ellen put potato chips and napkins on the table. What did she forget to do?_____

13. Mark asked Chuck to wrap the present, mail the letter, and clean the kitchen. Chuck mailed the letter and cleaned the kitchen. What did he forget to do?

    _____

14. Carla asked Dave to vacuum the rug, clean the sink, and open the windows. Dave opened the windows and cleaned the sink. What did he forget to do?

    _____

15. Mother asked Charlie to feed the dog, take out the garbage, and water the plants. Charlie took out the garbage and watered the plants. What did he forget to do?

    _____

ACTIVITY 22 - IDENTIFYING INCORRECT INFORMATION

Name:_____ Date:_____

Instructions: The child's task is to identify incorrect information by responding "yes" or "no" to each question. Have the child provide the correct information when he/she responds "no" to a question.

___ 1. The cat knocked over the bucket.

Did the cat knock over the bag?

___ 2. Mark put his book on the chair.

Did Mark put his coat on the chair?

___ 3. The small dog chased the large rat.

Did the dog chase a rat?

___ 4. The box was under the jar.

Was the jar under the box?

___ 5. Terry ran to the market before the game.

Did Terry run to the market before the movie?

___ 6. The pretty box was under an ugly lamp.

Was the box beside the lamp?

___ 7. Carol ate two sandwiches before school.

Did Carol eat two sandwiches before school?

___ 8. The cart bumped into a pole at the store.

Did the cart bump into a pole at the park?

___ 9. Lisa sang a song at a neighbor's house.

Did Lisa sing a song at a cousin's house?

___10. Steven bought a soda for Peter.

Did Peter buy a soda for Steven?

___11. Chris got his hair cut short after work.

Did Chris get his hair cut short after work?

___12. Amy lost her coat and dropped the cup.

Did Amy lose her cup and drop her coat?

___13. Sandy put her old shoes outside the house.

Did Sandy put her old shoes inside the house?

Copyright © 1997 by Academic Communication Associates. This form may be reproduced.

___14. Ellen cooked eggs and bacon for breakfast.

Did Ellen cook sausage and eggs for breakfast?

___15. Kathy closed the door and opened the window.

Did Kathy open the window and close the door?

___16. Sandy turned off the computer before leaving the room.

Did Sandy turn off the oven before leaving the room?

___17. Sam put a black shoe and a red shoe in the car.

Did Sam put a black shoe and a brown shoe in the car?

___18. Andy was holding a shoe and a sock in the garage.

Was Andy holding a shoe and a shirt in the garage?

___19. Luisa ate a peanut butter and jelly sandwich.

Did Luisa eat a peanut butter and honey sandwich.

___20. Cindy was holding a cup and a bag.

Was Cindy holding a bag and a cup?

___21. Mario was playing on the playground at school.

Was Mario playing on the playground at the park?

___22. Mrs. Smith had three boxes of pencils in her office.

Did Mrs. Smith have four boxes of pencils in her office?

___23. Nathan was riding a bicycle around the block.

Was Nathan riding a motorcycle around the block?

___24. Sam cooked hamburgers in his kitchen late at night.

Did Sam cook hamburgers in his kitchen early one afternoon?

___25. Mary arrived at the office at three o'clock.

Did Mary arrive at the hardware store at three o'clock?

___26. Carol painted the chair green after going to the market.

Did Carol paint the chair brown after going to the market?

___27. Betsy used a vacuum cleaner to clean the floor after the party?

Did Betsy use a mop to clean the floor after the party.

___28. The rabbit jumped over the box and ran across the yard.

Did the rabbit jump over the bike and run across the yard?

___29. The window in Carla's classroom cracked when she opened it.

Did the window in Carla's classroom crack when she closed it?

___30. Mitch was sleeping in the car when he heard a shout.

Was Mitch sleeping in the house when he heard a shout?

___31. Arnold planted a tree in the garden near the park.

Did Arnold plant a tree in the garden near the farm?

___32. Victor sold his car because he needed money to pay his bills.

Did Victor sell his house because he needed money to pay his bills?

___33. Patty ran to the store because her car was not working.

Did Patty run to the store because her bike was not working?

ACTIVITY 23 - LISTENING AND ASKING QUESTIONS

Name:_____ Date:_____

Instructions: A statement is presented orally and the child is asked to formulate a question about what was said. Record the child's response in the space provided.

1. Mark has new pants and a new shirt. Ask him where he got them.

   _____

2. Sandy went to the park with a friend. Ask her the name of the friend.

   _____

3. Cindy is going to the movie today. Ask her when she will come back.

   _____

4. Tom found the book that he was looking for. Ask him where he found it.

   _____

5. Lisa wants to go to the store. Ask her when she will go.

   _____

6. Martha needs new clothes for school. Ask her if she needs a new sweater.

   _____

7. Sarah went to the park to play. Ask her what she played at the park.

   _____

8. Kim went to a restaurant. Ask her what she ate.

   _____

9. Sam got a birthday present. Ask him where the present came from.

   _____

10. Carlos saw something in the box. Ask him what he saw.

    _____

Copyright © 1997 by Academic Communication Associates. This form may be reproduced.

11. Sandy needs to go to the doctor's office. Ask her where the doctor's office is.

———————————————————————————————————

12. Tina doesn't want to be late for a meeting. Ask her when the meeting starts.

———————————————————————————————————

13. Mindy is watching television. Ask her what she is watching on television.

———————————————————————————————————

14. Ken gave his new toy to a friend. Ask him who the friend is.

———————————————————————————————————

15. Marty is looking at a book. Ask him what book he is looking at.

———————————————————————————————————

ACTIVITY 24 - ANSWERING QUESTIONS ABOUT A SITUATION

Name: _____   Date:_____

Instructions: A sentence is read to the child and he/she is asked to respond to questions about the information presented in the sentence.

1. Martha went to the store with her mother.

    ___Where did Martha go?   _____

    ___Who went with Martha?   _____

2. Mark ate pizza and salad after the baseball game.

    ___When did Mark eat?   _____

    ___What did Mark eat?   _____

3. Donna planted seeds to grow carrots and corn in grandmother's yard.

    ___What kinds of seeds did Donna plant?   _____

    ___Where did Donna plant the seeds?   _____

4. Jeff saw a movie about a bear. The bear got lost and couldn't find his way home.

    ___What animal was in the movie?   _____

    ___What happened to the bear?   _____

5. Danny popped a balloon at the party. The noise woke up a baby.

    ___What did Danny do at the party?   _____

    ___Who woke up?   _____

6. Walter put on a green shirt before sweeping the yard?

    ___What did Walter put on?   _____

    ___What did Walter do after putting on the shirt? _____

7. Tom threw the ball and it went over the fence.

    ___Who threw the ball?   _____

    ___What happened to the ball after he threw it? _____

8. Bill cut the envelope in half and threw it in the trash.

    ___What did Bill cut?   _____

    ___What did Bill do after cutting the envelope? _____

Copyright © 1997 by Academic Communication Associates. This form may be reproduced.

9. Dan's bike got a flat tire and he had to walk all the way home.

What happened to Dan's bike? _____

How did Dan get home? _____

10. Tom went to the drugstore to buy some bandages.

Where did Tom go? _____

What did Tom buy? _____

ACTIVITY 25 - IDENTIFYING THE SETTING

Name: _____   Date: _____

Instructions: A sentence is read to the child and he/she is asked to identify where the "action" in the sentence takes place.

1. Mr. Casas is putting a carton of milk in his shopping cart.

   Where is he?   _____

2. Tommy is sitting at his desk listening to the teacher.

   Where is he?   _____

3. Maria is playing in the sand and watching the waves.

   Where is she?   _____

4. Ms. Jones hands the box that she wants to mail to a lady. The lady weighs the box and puts postage on it.

   Where is she?   _____

5. Tina is putting money into the slot to start the washing machine.

   Where is she?   _____

6. Andy is playing in the sandbox and on the swings.

   Where is he?   _____

7. Carla has a sore tooth. Dr. Hayward looks into her mouth.

   Where is she?   _____

8. Sylvia is telling the waiter that she would like to order spaghetti.

   Where is she?   _____

9. Marla is riding her sled.

   Where is she?   _____

Copyright © 1997 by Academic Communication Associates. This form may be reproduced.

10. Daniel jumped off the diving board and is swimming fast.

    Where is he?   _____

11. Betty sees clowns juggling and animals doing tricks.

    Where is she?   _____

12. Eddie throws the ball into the basket. His team wins the game.

    Where is he?   _____

13. Tim is wearing his pajamas and his mother is reading him a story.

    Where is he?   _____

14. Mary is riding on the roller coaster.

    Where is she?   _____

15. Mr. Edwards is buying wood, nails, and a hammer.

    Where is he?   _____

16. Cindy is trying to catch a fish with her new fishing pole.

    Where is she?   _____

17. Brandon is looking at lions, tigers, and other animals in cages.

    Where is he?   _____

18. Daniel is watching a movie on a large screen in a big room. The room is dark.

    Where is he?   _____

19. Bob is skating in a large room. He falls on the ice.

    Where is he?   _____

20. Linda is wearing pajamas. Her head is on a pillow.

    Where is she?   _____

ACTIVITY 26 - LISTENING FOR STORY SEQUENCE

Name: _____   Date:_____

Instructions: The following short stories stress the concepts *before* and *after*. First read the short story to the child. Then have the child answer the questions that follow. Remind the child to listen very carefully.

1. Lisa went to the grocery store after her visit to the post office. Before she put her grocery bags in her car, she had to unlock her trunk.

   ___A. What did Lisa do before she put her bags in her car?

   ___B. Where did Lisa go after she went to the post office?

2. Before Tommy ate the piece of cake, he washed his hands. He drank some milk after he finished his cake.

   ___A. Did Tommy eat his cake before or after he washed his hands?

   ___B. After he finished his cake, what did Tommy do?

3. Carol fixed the bed after she washed her hair. Before washing the clothes, Carol cleaned the kitchen.

   ___A. What did Carol do after she washed her hair?

   ___B. When did Carol clean the kitchen?

4. Before Carlos went to the library, he picked up his books. Carlos went to the pizza shop after he went to the library.

   ___A. What did Carlos do before he went to the library?

   ___B. Where did Carlos go after he went to the library?

5. Before eating the cotton candy, Ann ate a whole bag of popcorn. Ann got a stomach ache after she got home from the fair.

   ___A. When did Ann eat a whole bag of popcorn?

   ___B. When did Ann get a stomach ache?

Copyright © 1997 by Academic Communication Associates. This form may be reproduced.

6. Jason rode his bike to the park before the sun went down. After watching the sun go down, Jason rode back home.

   ___A. When did Jason ride to the park?

   ___B. When did Jason ride back home?

7. Nina ate lunch before the movie. After the movie, she ate some ice cream.

   ___A. When did Nina eat lunch?

   ___B. What did Nina eat after the movie?

8. Tyler drank some water before the game. He drank a soda after the game.

   ___A. What did Tyler drink before the game?

   ___B. When did Tyler drink the soda?

9. Maria washed her face before she brushed her teeth. She brushed her hair after she put on her lipstick.

   ___A. What did Maria do after she brushed her hair?

   ___B. When did Maria wash her face?

10. Zachary started to cry after he lost his puppy. The puppy was gone for ten days before it was found.

    ___A. How long was the puppy gone before it was found?

    ___B. When did Zachary start to cry?

11. Betty slid down the slide before she ran to the swing set. She played on the monkey bars after she climbed to the top.

    ___A. What did Betty do before she ran to the swing set?

    ___B. What did Betty do after she played on the monkey bars?

12. John looked at the clock before he started the test. After he finished the test, he put his pencil down on the desk.

    ___A. What did John do after he finished the test?

    ___B. When did John look at the clock?

13. The cat licked its paws after eating the fish. Before it took a nap, the cat drank some milk.

    ___A. What did the cat do after it ate the fish?

    ___B. When did the cat drink some milk?

14. After she saved up enough money, Dinah bought a bird at the pet shop. Before she took the bird home, Dinah had to buy a bird cage.

    ___A. What did Dinah buy after she saved her money?

    ___B. When did Dinah have to buy a bird cage?

15. Frank read the newspaper before he ate breakfast. After breakfast, he ran two miles.

    ___A. What did Frank do after he ate breakfast?

    ___B. When did Frank read the newspaper?

PART 2
LOOK AND LISTEN

This section includes 20 reproducible worksheets that can be used to build both listening and speaking skills. Each worksheet includes two pictures and four or more questions related to the content of the pictures. The first two questions require the child to listen to an auditory stimulus and to point to the picture being described. Questions requiring verbal responses provide the child with practice in using vocabulary, making comparisons, categorizing items, etc. A variety of activities can be created using these worksheets. Examples are the following:

1. Ask the child to compare specific nouns in the pictures with items in his/her home.

2. Ask the child to describe experiences he/she has had that are similar to those depicted in the picture. When showing the bear with the big smile (see page 74), for example, the teacher might ask the student to describe things that cause him/her to smile.

3. Present a story starter relating to the nouns shown in the picture and ask the student to finish the story.

Name:_____ Date:_____

Instructions: The child's task is to follow directions and answer questions about the pictures below.

1. Point to the animal that is crying.

2. Point to the animal that is sitting on a chair.

3. Name two other types of furniture.

4. Why do you think the fish is crying?

Copyright © 1997 by Academic Communication Associates. This form may be reproduced.

LOOK AND LISTEN

Name:_____ Date:_____

Instructions: The child's task is to follow directions and answer questions about the pictures below.

1. Point to the animal that is singing.

2. Point to the animal that is waving.

3. How are the zebra and the tiger alike?

4. Where do these two animals live?

Copyright © 1997 by Academic Communication Associates. This form may be reproduced.

Name:_____ Date:_____

Instructions: The child's task is to follow directions and answer questions about the pictures below.

1. Point to the martian that is in the spaceship.

2. Point to the martian that is in front of the spaceship.

3. Where do you think a martian comes from?

4. Where does a spaceship fly?

Copyright © 1997 by Academic Communication Associates. This form may be reproduced.

LOOK AND LISTEN

Name:_____ Date:_____

Instructions: The child's task is to follow directions and answer questions about the pictures below.

1. Point to the bear that is under the beehive.

2. Point to the bear that is over the beehive.

3. What do you think the bear is trying to do?

4. There is something in these pictures that makes a buzzing sound. What is it?

Copyright © 1997 by Academic Communication Associates. This form may be reproduced.

LOOK AND LISTEN

Name:_____ Date:_____

Instructions: The child's task is to follow directions and answer questions about the pictures below.

 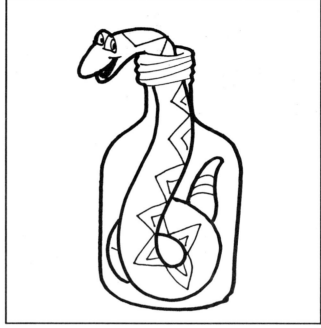

1. Point to the snake that is wrapped around the bottle.

2. Point to the snake that is inside the bottle.

3. Why do you think we can still see the snake in the bottle?

4. How do you think the snake will get out of the bottle?

Copyright © 1997 by Academic Communication Associates. This form may be reproduced.

LOOK AND LISTEN

Name:_____ Date:_____

Instructions: The child's task is to follow directions and answer questions about the pictures below.

1. Point to the jar that is open.

2. Point to the jar that is closed.

3. Name two foods that come in jars.

4. If you want to get something out of a jar, do you open or close it?

Copyright © 1997 by Academic Communication Associates. This form may be reproduced.

LOOK AND LISTEN

Name:_____ Date:_____

Instructions: The child's task is to follow directions and answer questions about the pictures below.

1. Point to the dog that is sitting next to a mouse.

2. Point to the dog that is beside a lizard.

3. Is the dog larger or smaller than a mouse?

4. What is another word for large? What is another word for small?

Copyright © 1997 by Academic Communication Associates. This form may be reproduced.

LOOK AND LISTEN

Name:_____ Date:_____

Instructions: The child's task is to follow directions and answer questions about the pictures below.

1. Point to the rabbit that is in the box.

2. Point to the rabbit that is behind the box.

3. Do you think you could fit in the box that the rabbit is in?

4. Does a rabbit have smaller ears than a dog?

Copyright © 1997 by Academic Communication Associates. This form may be reproduced.

LOOK AND LISTEN

Name:_____ Date:_____

Instructions: The child's task is to follow directions and answer questions about the pictures below.

1. Point to the shoelaces that are tied.

2. Point to the shoelaces that are untied.

3. What type of shoe do you think is pictured?

4. Should you wear shoes with laces that are tied or untied?

Copyright © 1997 by Academic Communication Associates. This form may be reproduced.

LOOK AND LISTEN

Name:_____ Date:_____

Instructions: The child's task is to follow directions and answer questions about the pictures below.

1. Point to the animal that is dancing.

2. Point to the animal that is smiling.

3. Do you think a dog can really dance? Why or why not?

4. The smiling bear has a very nice smile. Would an angry bear have a big smile?

Copyright © 1997 by Academic Communication Associates. This form may be reproduced.

LOOK AND LISTEN

Name:_____ Date:_____

Instructions: The child's task is to follow directions and answer questions about the pictures below.

1. Point to the bird that is flying above the balloon.

2. Point to the bird that is flying below the butterfly.

3. In the first picture, what is below the bird?

4. In what way is a bird the same as a butterfly?

Copyright © 1997 by Academic Communication Associates. This form may be reproduced.

LOOK AND LISTEN

Name:_____ Date:_____

Instructions: The child's task is to follow directions and answer questions about the pictures below.

1. Point to the boy who is eating spaghetti.

2. Point to the boy who is drinking.

3. What is the boy drinking?

4. How is spaghetti different from macaroni?

Copyright © 1997 by Academic Communication Associates. This form may be reproduced.

LOOK AND LISTEN

Name:_____ Date:_____

Instructions: The child's task is to follow directions and answer questions about the pictures below.

1. Point to the flower that has only two petals.

2. Point to the flower that has five petals.

3. What is the flower growing in?

4. What does a flower need to help it grow?

Copyright © 1997 by Academic Communication Associates. This form may be reproduced.

LOOK AND LISTEN

Name:_____ Date:_____

Instructions: The child's task is to follow directions and answer questions about the pictures below.

1. Point to the picture that has the most animals in it.

2. Point to the picture of the chicks.

3. Point to the picture of the cub. What is the mother called?

4. Where do chickens live?

Copyright © 1997 by Academic Communication Associates. This form may be reproduced.

Name:_____ Date:_____

Instructions: The child's task is to follow directions and answer questions about the pictures below.

1. Point to the shirt that has buttons on it. What are buttons for?

2. Point to the shirt that has short sleeves.

3. Which shirt would you wear on a very hot day?

4. How is a button like a zipper?

Copyright © 1997 by Academic Communication Associates. This form may be reproduced.

LOOK AND LISTEN

Name:_____ Date:_____

Instructions: The child's task is to follow directions and answer questions about the pictures below.

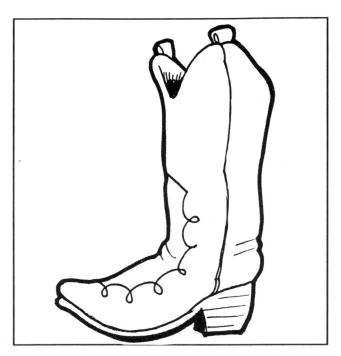 

1. Point to the shoe that is worn with pajamas.

2. Point to the shoe that a cowboy would wear.

3. Point to the shoe with the bow on it.

4. Which shoe would you wear outside?

Copyright © 1997 by Academic Communication Associates. This form may be reproduced.

LOOK AND LISTEN

Name:_____ Date:_____

Instructions: The child's task is to follow directions and answer questions about the pictures below.

1. Point to the person who is wearing a hat.

2. Point to the person who is wearing earrings.

3. Do you think the person wearing a hat is a mom?

4. Name something that the woman would wear on her face.

Copyright © 1997 by Academic Communication Associates. This form may be reproduced.

LOOK AND LISTEN

Name:_____ Date:_____

Instructions: The child's task is to follow directions and answer questions about the pictures below.

1. Point to the book that is closed.

2. Point to the book that is open.

3. What do you see inside of a book?

4. Name two things that people read.

Copyright © 1997 by Academic Communication Associates. This form may be reproduced.

LOOK AND LISTEN

Name:_____ Date:_____

Instructions: The child's task is to follow directions and answer questions about the pictures below.

1. Point to the person who is driving.

2. Point to the person who is reading.

3. What is the girl reading?

4. What is the woman driving?

Copyright © 1997 by Academic Communication Associates. This form may be reproduced.

LOOK AND LISTEN

Name:_____ Date:_____

Instructions: The child's task is to follow directions and answer questions about the pictures below.

1. Point to the animal that is writing.

2. Point to the animal that is skating.

3. What do you think the animal is writing?

4. Where do boys and girls go skating?

Copyright © 1997 by Academic Communication Associates. This form may be reproduced.

PART 3
STORY FUN

This section includes 10 short stories. Each story is followed by story recall questions. Encourage students to listen carefully so that they can answer the questions that follow each story. The first two activities include pictures of story characters that children can cut out. Children are asked to follow the teacher's directions for coloring and dressing these characters.

After the child has answered the questions that follow the story, ask him/her to retell that story. Present prompts, as necessary, to elicit additional information.

ACTIVITY I - ADVENTURES WITH CAMPY CAT

Name:_____ Date:_____

Instructions: Read the following short stories to the child. The child's task is to answer the questions that follow each story.

Story 1
Campy Cat Goes Camping

Campy Cat went camping with Buster Bear. They caught fish at the lake. They ate fish for dinner. After dinner, Campy and Buster went hiking.

Questions

1. Where did Campy Cat and Buster Bear go?

_____

2. What did they catch at the lake?

_____

3. When did they eat fish?

_____

4. What did Campy and Buster do after dinner?

_____

Copyright © 1997 by Academic Communication Associates. This form may be reproduced.

Name:_____ Date:_____

Story 2
Campy Goes to a Party

Campy wants to go to a party at his friend's house. The party will start at two o'clock. Before going to the party, Campy needs to take a shower, brush his teeth, and get dressed in his new clothes.

Questions

1. Where does Campy want to go?

   _____

2. When will the party start?

   _____

3. What does Campy need to do before going to the party.

   _____

Listening and Following Directions

Instructions: The picture of Campy Cat on the following page should be reproduced for this activity. Photocopy the page onto a piece of heavy stock or have the child glue the page onto a piece of construction paper. Then present the child with the instructions below.

1. Color Campy Cat's hat blue.
2. Color his pants brown and color his shoes black.
3. Draw red and blue stripes on his shirt.
4. Cut out the picture of Campy Cat with a pair of scissors.
5. Now cut out all of the clothing.
6. Paste the hat on his head; then paste the shoes on his feet.
7. Paste on the pants; then paste on the shirt.

Copyright © 1997 by Academic Communication Associates. This form may be reproduced.

Listening and Following Directions
Campy Goes to a Party

Have the child cut out the clothing and dress Campy Cat for the party. Present the instructions for cutting and coloring that follow the story. Remind the child to listen carefully and to follow your directions.

Copyright © 1997 by Academic Communication Associates. This form may be reproduced.

Present verbal instructions using the Campy Cat doll that the child has created. Examples are presented below:

1. Put Campy Cat behind the chair.
2. Put Campy Cat under the table.
3. Put Campy Cat in the box after picking up your pencil.
4. Put Campy Cat behind your head; then walk to the door.
5. Touch Campy's hat; then put him in the box.

Copyright © 1997 by Academic Communication Associates. This form may be reproduced.

ACTIVITY 2 - ADVENTURES WITH MARY MOUSE

Name:_____ Date:_____

Instructions: Read the following short story to the child. The child's task is to answer the questions that follow the story.

Story 1
Mary's New House

Mary Mouse lived in a big, yellow and blue house. Her house was the largest in the neighborhood. Mary always had parties at her house. She invited all of her friends.

Questions

1. What colors was Mary Mouse's house?

   _____

2. Was Mary's house the smallest or the largest?

   _____

3. What did Mary always do at her house?

   _____

4. Who did Mary Mouse invite to her house?

   _____

Copyright © 1997 by Academic Communication Associates. This form may be reproduced.

Name:_____ Date:_____

Story 2
Mary Mouse Gets Dressed Up

Mary Mouse is going to a costume party on Friday night at eight o'clock. She is going to wear a long dress and a necklace. She will wear a ribbon in her hair and a new pair of shoes. Mary plans to bring a chocolate cake to the party to share with all of her friends.

Questions

1. Where is Mary Mouse going?

   _____

2. When will she go to the party?

   _____

3. What will she wear to the party?

   _____

4. What will she share with her friends?

   _____

Listening and Following Directions

Instructions: The picture of Mary Mouse on the following page should be reproduced for this activity. Photocopy the page onto a piece of heavy stock or have the child glue the page onto a piece of construction paper. Then present the child with the instructions below.

1. Color Mary's ribbon blue.
2. Color her dress green and color her shoes red.
3. Draw a necklace around her neck. Use blue or gold to draw the necklace.
4. Cut out the picture of Mary Mouse with a pair of scissors.
5. Now cut out all of the clothing.
6. Paste the dress on before pasting the ribbon on her hair.
7. Now paste on the shoes.

Copyright © 1997 by Academic Communication Associates. This form may be reproduced.

Listening and Following Directions
Mary Gets Dressed Up

Have the child cut out the clothing and dress Mary Mouse for the party. Present the instructions for cutting and coloring that follow the story. Remind the child to listen carefully and to follow your directions.

Copyright © 1997 by Academic Communication Associates. This form may be reproduced.

ACTIVITY 3 - CARLOS AND THE DUCKS

Name:_____ Date:_____

Instructions: Read the following short story to the child. The child's task is to answer the questions that follow the story.

     Carlos ran to the park. He wanted to feed the ducks some bread. There were four ducks at the park pond. The ducks were very hungry.

Questions

1. Where did Carlos go?

   _____

2. What did Carlos want to feed to the ducks?

   _____

3. How many ducks were at the pond?

   _____

4. Were the ducks thirsty or hungry?

   _____

Copyright © 1997 by Academic Communication Associates. This form may be reproduced.

ACTIVITY 4 - THE CHERRY PIE

Name:_____ Date:_____

Instructions: Read the following short story to the child. The child's task is to answer the questions that follow the story.

    Mary baked a cherry pie. The pie had two pounds of cherries in it. Mary served her cherry pie with vanilla ice cream for dessert. Everyone thought the dessert tasted very good.

Questions

1. What kind of pie did Mary bake?

_____

2. How many pounds of cherries were in the pie?

_____

3. What did Mary serve for dessert?

_____

4. What did everyone think about the dessert?

_____

Copyright © 1997 by Academic Communication Associates. This form may be reproduced.

ACTIVITY 5 - LARRY LIZARD

Name:_____ Date:_____

Instructions: Read the following short story to the child. The child's task is to answer the questions that follow the story.

Larry Lizard lived under a leaf in a garden. He ate bugs for dinner. Larry's favorite bugs to eat were flies. Larry found many flies in the garden.

Questions

1. Where did Larry Lizard live?

   _____

2. What did Larry eat for dinner?

   _____

3. What was Larry's favorite bug to eat?

   _____

4. Where did Larry find many flies?

   _____

Copyright © 1997 by Academic Communication Associates. This form may be reproduced.

ACTIVITY 6 - AT THE MOVIES

Name:_____ Date:_____

Instructions: Read the following short story to the child. The child's task is to answer the questions that follow the story.

Shirley went to the movies with Ben. They ate peanuts and popcorn at the movies. They saw a very scary movie. The movie was about a monster that lived in the sea. The monster ate whales for dinner.

Questions

1. Who did Shirley go to the movies with?

   _____

2. What did they eat at the movies?

   _____

3. What kind of movie did they see?

   _____

4. What did the monster eat for dinner?

   _____

Copyright © 1997 by Academic Communication Associates. This form may be reproduced.

ACTIVITY 7 - GOING SHOPPING

Name:_____ Date:_____

Instructions: Read the following short story to the child. The child's task is to answer the questions that follow the story.

Rodney had five dollars to spend. He needed to buy a gift for his best friend's birthday. Rodney's best friend is Brad. Rodney likes the same things that Brad likes. He decided to buy Brad a fishing pole.

Questions

1. How much money did Rodney have?

_____

2. What did Rodney need to buy?

_____

3. Who is Rodney's best friend?

_____

4. What did Rodney buy for Brad?

_____

Copyright © 1997 by Academic Communication Associates. This form may be reproduced.

ACTIVITY 8 - SWIMMING IN THE LAKE

Name:_____ Date:_____

Instructions: Read the following short story to the child. The child's task is to answer the questions that follow the story.

   Carol went swimming in the lake. She wore her pretty pink swimsuit. Carol swam with the ducks in the lake. She saw her friend, Lynn, in the water.

Questions

1. Where did Carol go swimming?

_____

2. What did Carol wear?

_____

3. What did Carol swim with?

_____

4. Who did Carol see in the water?

_____

Copyright © 1997 by Academic Communication Associates. This form may be reproduced.

ACTIVITY 9 - LOOKING FOR FOOD

Name:_____ Date:_____

Instructions: Read the following short story to the child. The child's task is to answer the questions that follow the story.

     Rusty Raccoon was looking for something to eat. He went to the basement to look for food. He found some pickles and jelly in the basement. Rusty ate the pickles and jelly with some rolls that he found in the kitchen.

Questions

1. What was Rusty Raccoon looking for?

  _____

2. Where did he go to look for food?

  _____

3. What did Rusty find in the basement?

  _____

4. What did he eat the pickles and jelly with?

  _____

Copyright © 1997 by Academic Communication Associates. This form may be reproduced.

ACTIVITY 10 - GOING TO THE LIBRARY

Name:_____ Date:_____

Instructions: Read the following short story to the child. The child's task is to answer the questions that follow the story.

Cecil Snake crawled down to the library. He loved to read all of the books. His favorite book was called *The Sneaky Snake*. He read it ten times.

Questions

1. Who crawled down to the library?

   _____

2. What did Cecil love to do?

   _____

3. What was his favorite book called?

   _____

4. How many times did he read it?

   _____

Copyright © 1997 by Academic Communication Associates. This form may be reproduced.

PART 4
ANIMAL ADVENTURE
WORKSHEETS

Each of the picture worksheets in this section depicts an animal character surrounded by six items familiar to the experience of young children. These worksheets should be photocopied prior to presenting the activities. The specific activities included within the worksheets are the following:

1. *Find the Word*. The child is asked to point to the appropriate picture after hearing a verbal description of the noun.

2. *Listen for the Word*. A story is read that includes all of the nouns pictured on the worksheet. The child is asked to raise his/her hand each time that a noun on the worksheet is named.

3. *Answer the Questions*. The child is asked to respond to questions relating to the events of the short story.

4. *Fix the Sentence*. The child is presented with sentences that contain information about the story that is incorrect. The child is asked to correct the errors in these sentences.

5. *Tell the Story*. The child is asked to retell the story.

6. *Finish the Story*. The child is presented with a story starter and is asked to finish the story.

ACTIVITY 1 - PAULY POLAR BEAR

Name: _____ Date: _____

Materials Needed: Picture Worksheet #1
    Nouns pictured on worksheet:
        shirt
        shoe
        pig
        cat
        ring
        necklace

Find the Word

Instructions: Place the worksheet in front of the child. Read each verbal stimulus below to the child and ask him/her to point to the pictured item being described.

___ 1. It is worn around the neck. (necklace)

___ 2. It is worn on the finger. (ring)

___ 3. It is worn on your foot. (shoe)

___ 4. It has sleeves. (shirt)

___ 5. It says "meow." (cat)

___ 6. It says "oink." (pig)

Listen for the Word

Instructions: Ask the student to listen to the story below and to raise his/her hand when a word pictured on the worksheet is heard. All of the pictured nouns are included in the story and are underlined.

    Pauly Polar Bear put on his favorite <u>shirt</u>. He could not wear his favorite pair of shoes because one <u>shoe</u> was missing.
    When Pauly got dressed, he went over to his neighbor's house. He had to feed the neighbor's pet <u>pig</u> and <u>cat</u>. He found a <u>ring</u> and a <u>necklace</u> on the kitchen floor in his neighbor's house. He put them in his pocket to keep them safe.

Copyright © 1997 by Academic Communication Associates. This form may be reproduced.

Picture Worksheet #1 - Copyright © 1997 by Academic Communication Associates. This page may be reproduced.

Answer the Questions

Instructions: Read the story to the child a second time and ask him/her to respond to the questions below.

1. Why couldn't Pauly wear his favorite pair of shoes?

   _____

   _____

2. What did Pauly do for his neighbor?

   _____

   _____

3. What did Pauly find on the neighbor's floor?

   _____

4. Where did he put the things that he found?

   _____

5. Why did Pauly put the necklace and ring in his pocket?

   _____

Fix the Sentence

Instructions: The sentences below contain information about the story that is incorrect. The child's task is to fix each sentence.

1. Pauly is a wolf.

   _____

2. Pauly went to his cousin's house.

   _____

3. Pauly found a watch on the floor.

   _____

4. Pauly put the necklace on the table.

   _____

Copyright © 1997 by Academic Communication Associates. This form may be reproduced.

Tell the Story

Instructions: The child's task is to retell the story about Pauly Polar Bear. Prompts may be presented. Record the child's story in the space below:

_____

_____

_____

_____

_____

_____

_____

_____

_____

ACTIVITY 2 - PITNEY PIG

Name:_____ Date:_____

Materials Needed: Picture Worksheet #2
   Nouns shown on worksheet:
      broom
      mop
      spaghetti
      salad
      oranges
      pear

Find the Word

Instructions: Place the worksheet in front of the child. Read each verbal stimulus below to the child and ask him/her to point to the pictured item being described.

___1. It is a yellow fruit. (pear)

___2. It is green and you eat it. (salad)

___3. It is long and thin. You put red sauce on top of it. (spaghetti)

___4. You sweep with it. (broom)

___5. You put it in water and clean with it. (mop)

___6. This fruit has the same name as its color. (oranges)

Listen for the Word

Instructions: Ask the student to listen to the story below and to raise his/her hand when a word pictured on the worksheet is heard. All of the pictured nouns are included in the story.

   Pitney Pig ate some <u>spaghetti</u> for dinner. He also had a very big <u>salad</u> with lots of dressing on it. For dessert, Pitney ate some <u>oranges</u> and a <u>pear</u>.
   Pitney was very sloppy. He made a big mess on the floor. After dinner, Pitney used a <u>broom</u> and a <u>mop</u> to clean the floor.

Copyright © 1997 by Academic Communication Associates. This form may be reproduced.

Picture Worksheet #2 - Copyright © 1997 by Academic Communication Associates. This page may be reproduced.

Answer the Questions

Instructions: Read the story to the child a second time and ask him/her to respond to the questions below.

1. What did Pitney Pig eat for dinner?

   _____

2. What did he have for dessert?

   _____

3. Was Pitney a very neat pig?

   _____

4. What did Pitney do after dinner?

   _____

   _____

5. Pitney Pig was sloppy. What does *sloppy* mean?

   _____

   _____

Fix the Sentence

Instructions: The sentences below contain information about the story that is incorrect. The child's task is to fix each sentence.

1. Pitney Pig ate steak for dinner.

   _____

2. For dessert Pitney ate fried eggs.

   _____

3. Pitney was very neat when he ate.

   _____

4. Pitney cleaned the floor with a hose.

   _____

Copyright © 1997 by Academic Communication Associates. This form may be reproduced.

Tell the Story

Instructions: The child's task is to retell the story about Pitney Pig. Prompts may be presented. Record the child's story in the space below:

_____

_____

_____

_____

_____

_____

_____

_____

_____

Finish the Story

Instructions: Read the story starter below and ask the child to finish the story.

Pitney Pig was going shopping for food. He needed to buy food for a party. Finish the story.

_____

_____

_____

_____

_____

_____

_____

_____

_____

Copyright © 1997 by Academic Communication Associates. This form may be reproduced.

ACTIVITY 3 - LYLE THE LION

Name:_____ Date:_____

Materials Needed: Picture Worksheet #3
Nouns shown on worksheet:

fish

crab

apple

banana

bat

duck

Find the Word

Instructions: Place the worksheet in front of the child. Read each verbal stimulus below to the child and ask him/her to point to the pictured item being described.

___1. This animal quacks. (duck)

___2. It has a peel. (banana)

___3. It is a red fruit. (apple)

___4. It flies at night. (bat)

___5. It has fins and lives in water. (fish)

___6. It crawls on the ground in the sand. (crab)

Listen for the Word

Instructions: Ask the student to listen to the story below and to raise his/her hand when a word pictured on the worksheet is heard. All of the pictured nouns are included in the story.

Lyle the Lion went fishing one day. He went to the pond to catch some <u>fish</u> for dinner. While he was fishing, Lyle saw a <u>crab</u> in the water. The <u>crab</u> was try-ing to steal Lyle's bait. Lyle threw his <u>banana</u> peel at the <u>crab</u>. The <u>crab</u> was scared away.

After five hours of fishing, Lyle had not caught a single <u>fish</u>. He ate an <u>apple</u> while watching a <u>duck</u> swim around in circles. When Lyle saw a <u>bat</u> fly out of the trees, he knew it was time to go home.

Copyright © 1997 by Academic Communication Associates. This form may be reproduced.

Picture Worksheet #3 - Copyright © 1997 by Academic Communication Associates. This page may be reproduced.

Answer the Questions

Instructions: Read the story to the child a second time and ask him/her to respond to the questions below.

1. What did Lyle the Lion do one day?

   _____

2. What did Lyle try to catch?

   _____

3. What did Lyle see in the water?

   _____

4. How did Lyle know it was time to go home?

   _____

   _____

Fix the Sentence

Instructions: The sentences below contain information about the story that is incorrect. The child's task is to fix each sentence.

1. Lyle was an elephant.

   _____

2. Lyle went hiking.

   _____

3. Lyle saw a seal in the water.

   _____

4. Lyle threw his apple at the crab.

   _____

5. Lyle ate a watermelon.

   _____

Tell the Story

Instructions: The child's task is to retell the story about Lyle the Lion. Prompts may be presented. Record the child's story in the space below:

_____

_____

_____

_____

_____

_____

_____

_____

Finish the Story

Instructions: Read the story starter below and ask the child to finish the story.

Lyle the Lion was fishing one day when he saw a shark near his fishing pole. Finish the story.

_____

_____

_____

_____

_____

_____

_____

_____

Copyright © 1997 by Academic Communication Associates. This form may be reproduced.

ACTIVITY 4 - ELLA THE ELEPHANT

Name:_____ Date:_____

Materials Needed: Picture Worksheet #4
  Nouns shown on worksheet:

  car

  peanuts

  popcorn

  soda

  milk

  bike

Find the Word

Instructions: Place the worksheet in front of the child. Read each verbal stimulus below to the child and ask him/her to point to the pictured item being described.

___1. You ride on it. It has no motor. (bike)

___2. It has a shell. (peanut)

___3. People put butter and salt on it. (popcorn)

___4. It comes from a cow. (milk)

___5. It is a sweet drink with bubbles. (soda)

___6. It has four wheels. (car)

Listen for the Word

Instructions: Ask the student to listen to the story below and to raise his/her hand when a word pictured on the worksheet is heard. All of the pictured nouns are included in the story.

　　　Ella the Elephant worked at the circus. She drove her <u>car</u> to the circus on Saturdays. She rode her <u>bike</u> on Sundays.
　　　Ella got to eat <u>peanuts</u> and <u>popcorn</u> every day at the circus. Instead of <u>soda</u>, Ella liked to drink <u>milk</u>. She carried her <u>milk</u> in a big cooler. Ella enjoyed working at the circus.

Copyright © 1997 by Academic Communication Associates. This form may be reproduced.

Picture Worksheet #4 - Copyright © 1997 by Academic Communication Associates. This page may be reproduced.

Answer the Questions

Instructions: Read the story to the child a second time and ask him/her to respond to the questions below.

1. Where did Ella work?

   _____

2. What forms of transportation did Ella use to go to work?

   _____

3. What did Ella eat every day at the circus?

   _____

4. What beverage did Ella like to drink?

   _____

Fix the Sentence

Instructions: The sentences below contain information about the story that is incorrect. The child's task is to fix each sentence.

1. Ella was a dinosaur.

   _____

2. Ella worked at the hospital.

   _____

3. Ella rode a motorcycle to work.

   _____

4. Ella liked to drink lemonade.

   _____

Tell the Story

Instructions: The child's task is to retell the story about Ella the Elephant. Prompts may be presented. Record the child's story in the space below:

_____

_____

_____

_____

_____

_____

_____

_____

_____

Finish the Story

Instructions: Read the story starter below and ask the child to finish the story.

Ella the Elephant was walking past a tree when her trunk got stuck in a branch. Finish the story.

_____

_____

_____

_____

_____

_____

_____

_____

_____

Copyright © 1997 by Academic Communication Associates. This form may be reproduced.

ACTIVITY 5 - RANDY RABBIT

Name:_____ Date:_____

Materials Needed: Picture Worksheet #5
   Nouns shown on worksheet:

   ice cream

   popsicle

   carrots

   radishes

   feather

   cloud

Find the Word

Instructions: Place the worksheet in front of the child. Read each verbal stimulus below to the child and ask him/her to point to the pictured item being described.

1. It is usually white and you see it in the sky. (cloud)
2. It comes from a bird. (feather)
3. You put it in a cone and eat it. (ice cream)
4. It comes on a stick and tastes like frozen juice. (popsicle)
5. They grow in the ground and are red. (radishes)
6. They grow in the ground and are orange. (carrots)

Listen for the Word

Instructions: Ask the student to listen to the story below and to raise his/her hand when a word pictured on the worksheet is heard. All of the pictured nouns are included in the story.

   Randy Rabbit was swinging on his tree swing. Randy was swinging so high that he almost touched the <u>clouds</u>. He watched a <u>feather</u> floating in the breeze. He was thinking about whether he should have an <u>ice cream</u> cone or a <u>popsicle</u> for a snack.
   Randy's mom brought out <u>carrots</u> and <u>radishes</u> for Randy's lunch. She said that Randy had to eat lunch before he had any snacks. Randy ate his lunch while he was on his swing.

Answer the Questions

Instructions: Read the story to the child a second time and ask him/her to respond to the questions below.

1. What was Randy doing?

   _____

2. What did he see floating in the breeze?

   _____

3. What did Randy think about?

   _____

4. What did Randy eat for lunch?

   _____

Fix the Sentence

Instructions: The sentences below contain information about the story that is incorrect. The child's task is to fix each sentence.

1. Randy was a raccoon.

   _____

2. Randy was swinging from a lamp.

   _____

3. He saw a leaf floating in the breeze.

   _____

4. He was thinking about having a pizza for a snack.

   _____

Tell the Story

Instructions: The child's task is to retell the story about Randy Rabbit. Prompts may be presented. Record the child's story in the space below:

_____

_____

_____

_____

_____

_____

_____

_____

Finish the Story

Instructions: Read the story starter below and ask the child to finish the story.

Randy Rabbit was eating a carrot when he saw a wolf. Finish the story.

_____

_____

_____

_____

_____

_____

_____

_____

Copyright © 1997 by Academic Communication Associates. This form may be reproduced.

ACTIVITY 6 - CARLA THE COW

Name:_____ Date:_____

Materials Needed: Picture Worksheet #6
   Nouns shown on worksheet:

   barn

   chickens

   fence

   pigs

   grass

   daisies

Find the Word

Instructions: Place the worksheet in front of the child. Read each verbal stimulus below to the child and ask him/her to point to the pictured item being described.

1. It is green and grows in the ground. (grass)
2. These flowers smell nice. (daisies)
3. These animals lay eggs. (chickens)
4. Horses sleep here. (barn)
5. These animals say "oink." (pigs)
6. This is put up around a farm to keep the animals from leaving. (fence)

Listen for the Word

Instructions: Ask the student to listen to the story below and to raise his/her hand when a word pictured on the worksheet is heard. All of the pictured nouns are included in the story.

   Carla the Cow lived on a farm with some <u>chickens</u> and <u>pigs</u>. The animals shared a <u>barn</u> in the middle of the farm. The farm was surrounded by a wooden <u>fence</u>. Carla would eat the <u>grass</u> around the farm. Sometimes she ate some <u>daisies</u> for a special treat.

Copyright © 1997 by Academic Communication Associates. This form may be reproduced.

Answer the Questions

Instructions: Read the story to the child a second time and ask him/her to respond to the questions below.

1. Where did Carla the Cow live?

   _____

2. What other animals lived on the farm?

   _____

3. What surrounded the barn?

   _____

4. What is a barn?

   _____

5. What did Carla like to eat?

   _____

Fix the Sentence

Instructions: The sentences below contain information about the story that is incorrect. The child's task is to fix each sentence.

1. Carla lived in a cave.

   _____

2. Carla was a rooster.

   _____

3. Carla liked to eat bananas.

   _____

Copyright © 1997 by Academic Communication Associates. This form may be reproduced.

Tell the Story

Instructions: The child's task is to retell the story about Carla the Cow. Prompts may be presented. Record the child's story in the space below:

_____

_____

_____

_____

_____

_____

_____

_____

_____

Finish the Story

Instructions: Read the story starter below and ask the child to finish the story.

Carla the Cow was sleeping in the barn when the chickens started to make a lot of noise. Finish the story.

_____

_____

_____

_____

_____

_____

_____

_____

Copyright © 1997 by Academic Communication Associates. This form may be reproduced.

ACTIVITY 7 - RUSTY RACCOON

Name:_____ Date:_____

Materials Needed: Picture Worksheet #7
  Nouns shown on worksheet:

     skateboard

     drums

     bus

     bowl

     chair

     spoon

Find the Word

Instructions: Place the worksheet in front of the child. Read each verbal stimulus below to the child and ask him/her to point to the pictured item being described.

1. You pour milk into this. (bowl)
2. You hit this with a stick. (drums)
3. This takes people to school. (bus)
4. You put your feet on this and go for a ride. (skateboard)
5. You eat cereal with this. (spoon)
6. You sit on this. (chair)

Listen for the Word

Instructions: Ask the student to listen to the story below and to raise his/her hand when a word pictured on the worksheet is heard. All of the pictured nouns are included in the story.

    Rusty Raccoon rode the <u>bus</u> home from school. He was hungry so he got a <u>bowl</u>, a <u>spoon</u>, cereal, and milk in the kitchen. He sat down in a <u>chair</u> and ate his cereal. After his snack, he hopped on a <u>skateboard</u> with <u>drums</u> in his hands. Rusty rushed to his friend's house.

    Rusty and his friend, Jason, played the <u>drums</u> until it was time for dinner. They wanted to form a band with their other friends.

Copyright © 1997 by Academic Communication Associates. This form may be reproduced.

Picture Worksheet #7 - Copyright © 1997 by Academic Communication Associates. This page may be reproduced.

Answer the Questions

Instructions: Read the story to the child a second time and ask him/her to respond to the questions below.

1. What did Rusty Raccoon do after he got home from school?

   _____

2. How did Rusty get to his friend's house?

   _____

3. Who was Rusty's friend?

   _____

4. What did Rusty and his friend want to do?

   _____

Fix the Sentence

Instructions: The sentences below contain information about the story that is incorrect. The child's task is to fix each sentence.

1. Rusty rode his wagon home from school.

   _____

2. Rusty played his drums until breakfast.

   _____

3. Rusty ate a pickle.

   _____

4. Randy carried his guitar when he was riding his bike.

   _____

Copyright © 1997 by Academic Communication Associates. This form may be reproduced.

Tell the Story

Instructions: The child's task is to retell the story about Rusty Raccoon. Prompts may be presented. Record the child's story in the space below:

_____

_____

_____

_____

_____

_____

_____

_____

Finish the Story

Instructions: Read the story starter below and ask the child to finish the story.

Rusty Raccoon was playing the drums in his house late at night when nobody was home. Finish the story.

_____

_____

_____

_____

_____

_____

_____

_____

_____

Copyright © 1997 by Academic Communication Associates. This form may be reproduced.

ACTIVITY 8 - MARY MOUSE

Name:_____ Date:_____

Materials Needed: Picture Worksheet #8
  Nouns shown on worksheet:

> snake
>
> sofa
>
> saw
>
> dress
>
> wrench
>
> faucet

Find the Word

Instructions: Place the worksheet in front of the child. Read each verbal stimulus below to the child and ask him/her to point to the pictured item being described.

1. It is used to cut wood. (saw)
2. It is used to turn on the water. (faucet)
3. It is worn by women. (dress)
4. It is long and crawls on the ground. (snake)
5. It is long and you sit on it. (sofa)
6. It is a tool that you use to tighten or loosen things. (wrench)

Listen for the Word

Instructions: Ask the student to listen to the story below and to raise his/her hand when a word pictured on the worksheet is heard. All of the pictured nouns are included in the story.

Mary Mouse was putting on her <u>dress</u> when she saw a big <u>snake</u>. The <u>snake</u> crawled under the <u>sofa</u>. Mary screamed and tripped over a <u>wrench</u> and a <u>saw</u>. The snake went outside and into the yard.

Mary turned the <u>faucet</u> on to get a drink of water. She was glad that the <u>snake</u> had gone outside.

Picture Worksheet #8 - Copyright © 1997 by Academic Communication Associates. This page may be reproduced.

Answer the Questions

Instructions: Read the story to the child a second time and ask him/her to respond to the questions below.

1. What did Mary Mouse see when she put on her dress?

    _____

2. Where did the snake crawl?

    _____

3. What did she trip over?

    _____

4. What did Mary do after the mouse went outside?

    _____

Fix the Sentence

Instructions: The sentences below contain information about the story that is incorrect. The child's task is to fix each sentence.

1. Mary Mouse saw a snake when she was putting on her hat.

    _____

2. Mary Mouse was not afraid of the snake.

    _____

3. Mary Mouse hid under the couch.

    _____

4. Mary Mouse crawled into the yard.

    _____

Tell the Story

Instructions: The child's task is to retell the story about Mary Mouse. Prompts may be presented. Record the child's story in the space below:

_____

_____

_____

_____

_____

_____

_____

_____

_____

Finish the Story

Instructions: Read the story starter below and ask the child to finish the story.

Mary Mouse was eating lunch when she saw a snake crawling on the kitchen table. Finish the story.

_____

_____

_____

_____

_____

_____

_____

_____

_____

Copyright © 1997 by Academic Communication Associates. This form may be reproduced.

ACTIVITY 9 - JASON THE BEAR

Name:_____ Date:_____

Materials Needed: Picture Worksheet #9
   Nouns shown on worksheet:

      ball

      shorts

      dog

      cooler

      umbrella

      shark

Find the Word

Instructions: Place the worksheet in front of the child. Read each verbal stimulus below to the child and ask him/her to point to the pictured item being described.

1. It protects us from the rain. (umbrella)
2. It is used to hold drinks. (cooler)
3. It has sharp teeth and lives in water. (shark)
4. It has a tail and four legs. (dog)
5. We wear these on hot days. (shorts)
6. It is round and bounces. (ball)

Listen for the Word

Instructions: Ask the child to listen to the story below and to raise his/her hand when a word pictured on the worksheet is heard. All of the pictured nouns are included in the story.

    Jason the Bear put his <u>shorts</u> on to go to the beach. He took his <u>dog</u>, Homer, with him. Jason also took a <u>cooler</u> and an <u>umbrella</u> to the beach.

    When Jason and Homer got to the beach, Jason put up the <u>umbrella</u>. He put his <u>cooler</u> under the <u>umbrella</u> in the shade.

    Jason and Homer ran into the water. They were having fun swimming until someone saw a <u>shark</u>. Everyone had to get out of the water when the shark was spotted. Jason decided to stay at the beach to watch the <u>shark</u> swim.

Copyright © 1997 by Academic Communication Associates. This form may be reproduced.

Answer the Questions

Instructions: Read the story to the child a second time and ask him/her to respond to the questions below.

1. What did Jason take to the beach?

   _____

2. What did Jason do as soon as he got to the beach?

   _____

3. Why did everyone have to get out of the water?

   _____

4. What did Jason decide to do?

   _____

Fix the Sentence

Instructions: The sentences below contain information about the story that is incorrect. The child's task is to fix each sentence.

1. Jason wore his boots to the beach.

   _____

2. Jason put his toaster under the umbrella.

   _____

3. Jason had fun swimming until he saw a tiger.

   _____

4. Jason's dog was named Rover.

   _____

Copyright © 1997 by Academic Communication Associates. This form may be reproduced.

Tell the Story

Instructions: The child's task is to retell the story about Jason the Bear. Prompts may be presented. Record the child's story in the space below:

_____

_____

_____

_____

_____

_____

_____

_____

Finish the Story

Instructions: Read the story starter below and ask the child to finish the story.

Jason the Bear was swimming in the water when he saw two giant sharks. Finish the story.

_____

_____

_____

_____

_____

_____

_____

_____

Copyright © 1997 by Academic Communication Associates. This form may be reproduced.

ACTIVITY 10 - DAWSON THE DOG

Name:_____ Date:_____

Materials Needed: Picture Worksheet #10
   Nouns shown on worksheet:

   pliers

   boat

   penguin

   table

   caterpillar

   knife

Find the Word

Instructions: Place the worksheet in front of the child. Read each verbal stimulus below to the child and ask him/her to point to the pictured item being described.

1. This insect turns into a butterfly. (caterpillar)
2. This animal swims in water. (penguin)
3. You ride this in the water. (boat)
4. We put food on this when we eat. (table)
5. You use this to tighten things. (pliers)
6. This is used to cut food. (knife)

Listen for the Word

Instructions: Ask the child to listen to the story below and to raise his/her hand when a word pictured on the worksheet is heard. All of the pictured nouns are included in the story.

   Dawson Dog was fixing his <u>boat</u> with a pair of <u>pliers</u>. His friend, Penny <u>Penguin</u>, was helping. She helped by getting any tool that Dawson needed out of his tool box.
   When Penny reached down to get a screwdriver, she screamed. Dawson turned around and saw a <u>caterpillar</u> on the <u>table</u>.

Copyright © 1997 by Academic Communication Associates. This form may be reproduced.

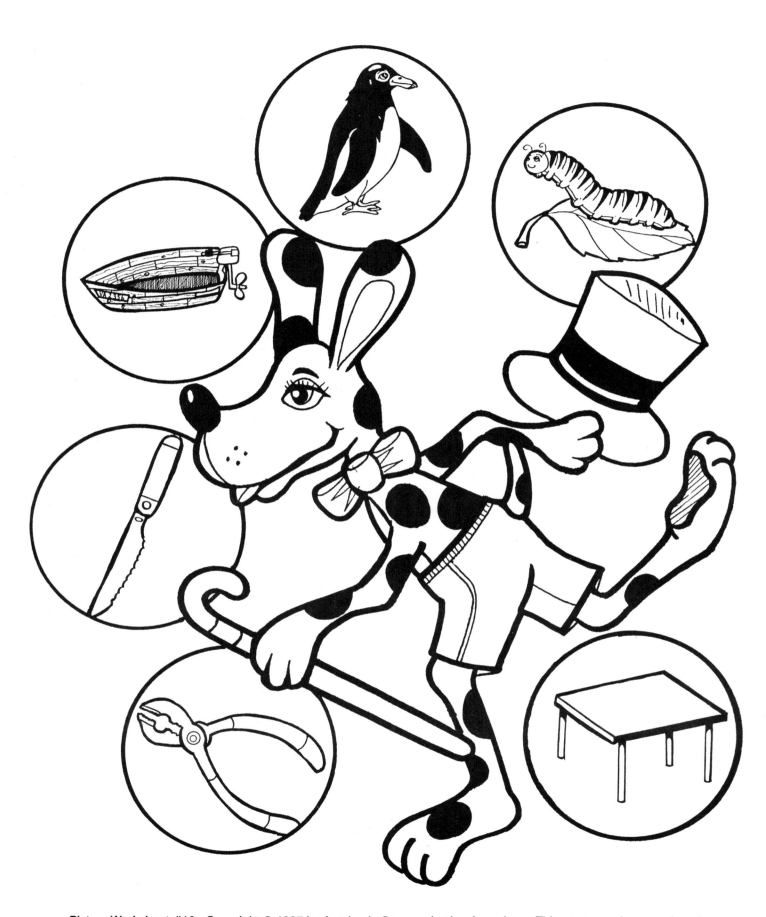

Picture Worksheet #10 - Copyright © 1997 by Academic Communication Associates. This page may be reproduced.

Penny picked up a <u>knife</u> to stab the <u>caterpillar</u>. When Dawson saw the <u>knife</u>, he yelled, "Please don't hurt my friend, Callie <u>Caterpillar</u>!"

After Dawson introduced Callie to Penny, Penny wasn't afraid of <u>caterpillars</u> anymore.

Answer the Questions

Instructions: Read the story to the child a second time and ask him/her to respond to the questions below.

1. What was Dawson Dog doing with the pliers?

   _____

2. Who was helping Dawson?

   _____

3. Why did Penny scream?

   _____

4. Who was Callie Caterpillar's friend?

   _____

Fix the Sentence

Instructions: The sentences below contain information about the story that is incorrect. The child's task is to fix each sentence.

1. Penny Porcupine was helping Dawson.

   _____

2. Dawson used pliers to fix his roof.

   _____

3. Penny Penguin saw a caterpillar in the toolbox.

   _____

4. Penny Penguin was happy when she saw the caterpillar.

   _____

Tell the Story

Instructions: The child's task is to retell the story about Dawson Dog. Prompts may be presented. Record the child's story in the space below:

_____

_____

_____

_____

_____

_____

_____

_____

_____

Finish the Story

Instructions: Read the story starter below and ask the child to finish the story.

Dawson Dog was fixing his boat when he heard a loud roar. Finish the story.

_____

_____

_____

_____

_____

_____

_____

_____

_____

Copyright © 1997 by Academic Communication Associates. This form may be reproduced.

PART 5
FUN WITH MOODS
AND FEELINGS

The happy face and sad face illustrations on the following pages are needed for all of the activities in this section. Copy the faces onto colored paper and glue them to a wooden stick. The happy face should be on one side of the stick and the sad face should be on the other.

In Activity 1, sentences are read to the child and he/she is asked to display the happy face when happy statements are heard; the sad face is to be displayed when sad statements are heard. In the remaining activities, the child is asked to identify happy and sad statements within short stories. After listening to each story, sentences are read that contain incorrect information about the story. The child's task is to "fix" these sentences. Following completion of this activity, it is recommended that the child be asked to retell the entire story.

Happy

Have the child turn this face into a happy face by drawing a smile on it.

The happy face and the sad face are used in all of the activities in this section. Reproduce the faces onto colored paper and glue them to a wooden stick. The happy face should be on one side of the stick and the sad face should be on the other.

Copyright © 1997 by Academic Communication Associates. This form may be reproduced.

Sad

Have the child turn this face into a sad face by drawing a frown on it.

Copyright © 1997 by Academic Communication Associates. This form may be reproduced.

ACTIVITY I - JASON'S BUSY DAY

Name:_____ Date:_____

Materials: Happy face and sad face pictures

Instructions: Read the sentences below. The child's task is to show the happy face whenever he/she hears a sentence about something that would make Jason the Bear feel good or happy. The sad face should be shown when the child hears a sentence about something that would make Jason the Bear feel bad or sad.

> *Say*: Jason the Bear is having a very busy day today. Show the happy face when you hear something that would make Jason feel happy. Show the sad face when you hear something that would make him feel sad.

1. Jason smelled fresh-baked cookies. ___Happy ___Sad
2. A bully is picking on Jason. ___Happy ___Sad
3. Someone takes away Jason's favorite toy. ___Happy ___Sad
4. Jason gets a great big hug. ___Happy ___Sad
5. Someone teases Jason. ___Happy ___Sad
6. Jason's pen runs out of ink. ___Happy ___Sad
7. Jason's mom makes liver and onions for breakfast. ___Happy ___Sad
8. Jason is watching his favorite cartoon show. ___Happy ___Sad
9. A friend gives Jason a present. ___Happy ___Sad
10. Jason finds a dime on the floor. ___Happy ___Sad
11. Jason's best friend moves away. ___Happy ___Sad
12. Jason's teacher says she's proud of him. ___Happy ___Sad
13. The sun shines through Jason's window. ___Happy ___Sad
14. The dentist says that Jason doesn't have any cavities. ___Happy ___Sad
15. A cute puppy is licking Jason's face. ___Happy ___Sad
16. Jason's sister eats all of his candy. ___Happy ___Sad
17. Jason is given a nice, shiny, red apple. ___Happy ___Sad
18. Jason gets lost at the mall. ___Happy ___Sad

Copyright © 1997 by Academic Communication Associates. This form may be reproduced.

ACTIVITY 2 - BUDDY BEAR CATCHES A FISH

Name:_____ Date:_____

Happy or Sad

Materials: Happy face and sad face pictures

Instructions: Read the story to the child. The child's task is to hold up the happy face when something happy is heard and the sad face when something sad is heard.

Buddy Bear went fishing in his favorite pond. He liked to go fishing every day. Buddy Bear liked fishing, but he didn't like putting a worm on the end of his hook. The worm didn't like it either.

Buddy Bear caught a very big fish. It was bigger than the smile on Buddy Bear's face. When Buddy took the fish off of the hook, he was sad. He just couldn't eat that fish. So Buddy Bear threw the fish back into the water. The fish was so happy that it thanked Buddy Bear.

Copyright © 1997 by Academic Communication Associates. This form may be reproduced.

1. What happy things happened in the story?

_____

_____

_____

2. What sad things happened in the story?

_____

_____

_____

Fix the Sentence

Instructions: The sentences below contain information about the story that is incorrect. The child's task is to fix each sentence.

1. Buddy Bear liked to go skiing every day.

_____

2. He liked to put worms on his hook.

_____

3. Buddy Bear caught a very small fish.

_____

4. Buddy Bear ate the fish.

_____

5. The fish was very sad.

_____

Copyright © 1997 by Academic Communication Associates. This form may be reproduced.

ACTIVITY 3 - THE BIG DOG

Name:_____ Date:_____

Happy or Sad

Materials: Happy face and sad face pictures

Instructions: Read the story to the child. The child's task is to hold up the happy face when something happy is heard and the sad face when something sad is heard.

    Sally skipped down the sidewalk. She sang a pretty song as she skipped. Before she could get away, a big dog started to jump on Sally. Sally was scared. Sally started to laugh when the dog licked her face.

1. What happy things happened in the story?

    _____

    _____

    _____

Copyright © 1997 by Academic Communication Associates. This form may be reproduced.

2. What sad things happened in the story?

_____

_____

_____

Fix the Sentence

Instructions: The sentences below contain information about the story that is incorrect. The child's task is to fix each sentence.

1. Sally jumped down the sidewalk.

_____

2. She sang a horrible song.

_____

3. A big cat jumped on Sally.

_____

4. Sally wasn't scared.

_____

5. Sally cried when the dog licked her face.

_____

ACTIVITY 4 - RODDY FINDS WATER

Name:_____ Date:_____

Happy or Sad

Materials: Happy face and sad face pictures

Instructions: Read the story to the child. The child's task is to hold up the happy face when something happy is heard and the sad face when something sad is heard.

It was very, very hot in the desert. There was no wind at all. Roddy Roadrunner was very thirsty. He needed some water. Just when Roddy thought he could no longer walk, he saw a large pool of water in front of him. He jumped into the water to cool off.

1. What happy things happened in the story?

_____

_____

_____

Copyright © 1997 by Academic Communication Associates. This form may be reproduced.

2. What sad things happened in the story?

_____

_____

_____

Fix the Sentence

Instructions: The sentences below contain information about the story that is incorrect. The child's task is to fix each sentence.

1. It was very cold in the desert.

_____

2. Everything was blowing in the wind.

_____

3. Roddy Roadrunner was very hungry.

_____

4. Roddy saw a pool of oil.

_____

5. He ran around the water.

_____

ACTIVITY 5 - MOREY THE MONKEY

Name:_____ Date:_____

Happy or Sad

Materials: Happy face and sad face pictures

Instructions: Read the story to the child. The child's task is to hold up the happy face when something happy is heard and the sad face when something sad is heard.

Morey was having a very rough day at the zoo. He was bored. He had no one to play with.

Morey tried to have fun. He blew bubbles, played ball, and even ate bananas. But nothing made him happy.

Morey decided to take a nap. When he woke up, he saw another monkey in his cage. It was Mary Monkey! This made Morey clap his hands. He had someone to play with.

Copyright © 1997 by Academic Communication Associates. This form may be reproduced.

1. What happy things happened in the story?

_____

_____

_____

2. What sad things happened in the story?

_____

_____

_____

Fix the Sentence

Instructions: The sentences below contain information about the story that is incorrect. The child's task is to fix each sentence.

1. Morey was having a fun day at the zoo.

_____

2. He had lots of friends to play with.

_____

3. Morey didn't take a nap.

_____

4. Mary Monkey was in Morey's dream.

_____

5. Morey was sad to see Mary.

_____

ACTIVITY 6 - A RAINY DAY FOR CHRISTOPHER

Name:_____ Date:_____

Happy or Sad

Materials: Happy face and sad face pictures

Instructions: Read the story to the child. The child's task is to hold up the happy face when something happy is heard and the sad face when something sad is heard.

Christopher was getting ready to go to the fair. All of a sudden, it started to rain. It rained very hard. Christopher waited in his room as the rain came down. He played with his toy cars in his room. He forgot all about the fair.

1. What happy things happened in the story?

_____

_____

_____

Copyright © 1997 by Academic Communication Associates. This form may be reproduced.

2. What sad things happened in the story?

_____

_____

_____

Fix the Sentence

Instructions: The sentences below contain information about the story that is incorrect. The child's task is to fix each sentence.

1. Christopher was getting ready to go to bed.

_____

2. It was very sunny outside.

_____

3. Christopher waited in the kitchen.

_____

4. He played in the rain.

_____

5. Christopher forgot about the circus.

_____

ACTIVITY 7 - THERESA GOES TO THE SUPERMARKET

Name:_____ Date:_____

Happy or Sad

Materials: Happy face and sad face pictures

Instructions: Read the story to the child. The child's task is to hold up the happy face when something happy is heard and the sad face when something sad is heard.

     Theresa needed three things on her grocery list. She needed some bread, milk, and coffee. She enjoyed going grocery shopping.
     When Theresa got home from the store, she found out that she forgot to buy bread.

1. What happy things happened in the story?

     _____

     _____

     _____

Copyright © 1997 by Academic Communication Associates. This form may be reproduced.

2. What sad things happened in the story?

_____

_____

_____

Fix the Sentence

Instructions: The sentences below contain information about the story that is incorrect. The child's task is to fix each sentence.

1. Theresa needed one thing at the grocery store.

_____

2. She needed some butter.

_____

3. Theresa hated to go grocery shopping.

_____

4. Theresa went to the library.

_____

5. She forgot to buy a book.

_____

ACTIVITY 8 - THE WHEELCHAIR RACE

Name:_____ Date:_____

Happy or Sad

Materials: Happy face and sad face pictures

Instructions: Read the story to the child. The child's task is to hold up the happy face when something happy is heard and the sad face when something sad is heard.

     When Lee broke his leg, he had to use a wheelchair. Lee thought riding in his wheelchair was fun. He rolled down hills as fast as he could.
     One day Lee saw Sara in her wheelchair. Lee found out that Sara would always need her wheelchair. Lee felt sorry for Sara.
     Sara thought riding down the hill was fun, too. She told Lee that she could beat him in a race. Lee was surprised that Sara wanted to race with him.
     Sara and Lee raced down the hill in their wheelchairs. Sara beat Lee down the hill! She was so excited that she almost fell over. Sara and Lee rode back up the hill as they talked and laughed. They had lots of fun.

Copyright © 1997 by Academic Communication Associates. This form may be reproduced.

1. What happy things happened in the story?

_____

_____

_____

2. What sad things happened in the story?

_____

_____

_____

Fix the Sentence

Instructions: The sentences below contain information about the story that is incorrect. The child's task is to fix each sentence.

1. Lee broke his arm.

_____

2. He didn't like riding in his wheelchair.

_____

3. Lee saw Amy in her wheelchair.

_____

4. Lee felt happy for Sara.

_____

ACTIVITY 9 - JERRY READS HIS BOOKS

Name:_____ Date:_____

Happy or Sad

Materials: Happy face and sad face pictures

Instructions: Read the story to the child. The child's task is to hold up the happy face when something happy is heard and the sad face when something sad is heard.

Jerry was having a very rough day. No one wanted to play with him. Everyone was too busy.

Jerry went into his room and looked around for something to do. He picked up some books and started reading. Jerry read for hours. Before he knew it, it was time for dinner.

Jerry told his family all about the books he read. He enjoyed them very much.

1. What happy things happened in the story?

_____

_____

Copyright © 1997 by Academic Communication Associates. This form may be reproduced.

2. What sad things happened in the story?

_____

_____

_____

Fix the Sentence

Instructions: The sentences below contain information about the story that is incorrect. The child's task is to fix each sentence.

1. Everyone wanted to play with Jerry.

_____

2. Jerry went into the dining room.

_____

3. Jerry read the newspaper.

_____

4. He read for five minutes.

_____

5. Jerry didn't like to read books.

_____

ACTIVITY 10 - TINA TURTLE NEEDS HELP

Name:_____ Date:_____

Happy or Sad

Materials: Happy face and sad face pictures

Instructions: Read the story to the child. The child's task is to hold up the happy face when something happy is heard and the sad face when something sad is heard.

     Tina Turtle rolled down a hill. She got stuck upside down. She looked around her and everything looked upside down.

     Tina cried, "Oh no, what am I going to do!"

     Tina heard footsteps. She looked up and saw a very tall man. The man looked at Tina and asked, "Do you need some help, little turtle?"

     Tina nodded her head. The man knew that Tina was in trouble.

     The man turned Tina over and patted her on her back. Tina was so happy. She thanked the man and started on her way back home.

Copyright © 1997 by Academic Communication Associates. This form may be reproduced.

1. What happy things happened in the story?

_____

_____

_____

2. What sad things happened in the story?

_____

_____

_____

Fix the Sentence

Instructions: The sentences below contain information about the story that is incorrect. The child's task is to fix each sentence.

1. Tina Turtle skipped down a hill.

_____

2. She got stuck in a big hole.

_____

3. She saw a very short woman.

_____

4. The man walked away.

_____

5. Tina didn't need any help.

_____

ACTIVITY II - SAMMY SKUNK HAS NO FRIENDS

Name:_____ Date:_____

Happy or Sad

Materials: Happy face and sad face pictures

Instructions: Read the story to the child. The child's task is to hold up the happy face when something happy is heard and the sad face when something sad is heard.

    Sammy Skunk didn't know why he had no friends. He tried to be nice to everyone he met. Everyone would run away from Sammy.

    One day Sammy saw a little girl crying. Sammy went over to the little girl to see what was the matter. The little girl looked up and said that she was sad because she lost her doll.

    Sammy found the doll in the bushes. This made the girl smile. Sammy was so glad that the girl didn't run away from him. He asked the girl if she would be his friend.

    "You found my doll so I'll be your friend!" said the girl.

Copyright © 1997 by Academic Communication Associates. This form may be reproduced.

1. What happy things happened in the story?

_____

_____

_____

2. What sad things happened in the story?

_____

_____

_____

Fix the Sentence

Instructions: The sentences below contain information about the story that is incorrect. The child's task is to fix each sentence.

1. Everyone wanted to be Sammy's friend.

_____

2. The little girl that Sammy saw was laughing.

_____

3. The little girl lost her necklace.

_____

4. The little girl ran away from Sammy.

_____

5. The little girl didn't like Sammy because he was a skunk.

_____

Appendix A
Picture Worksheets

The picture worksheets in this appendix are used with Activity 17 in Part 1 of this book. These worksheets may be reproduced for distribution to students.

Following Directions - Worksheet A

Name:_____ Date:_____

Copyright © 1997 by Academic Communication Associates. This form may be reproduced.

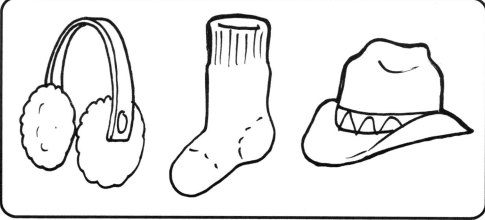

Following Directions - Worksheet B

Name:_____ Date:_____

Copyright © 1997 by Academic Communication Associates. This form may be reproduced.

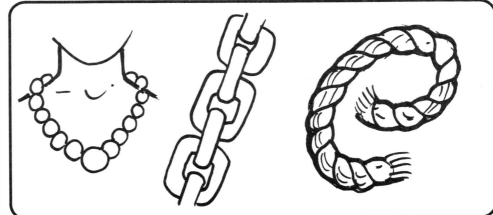

Following Directions - Worksheet C

Name:_____ Date:_____

Copyright © 1997 by Academic Communication Associates. This form may be reproduced.

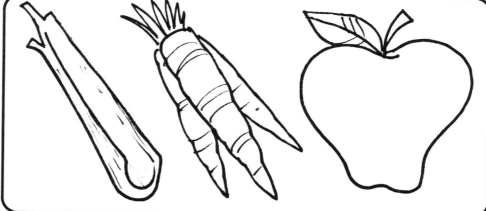

Following Directions - Worksheet D

Name:_____ Date:_____

Copyright © 1997 by Academic Communication Associates. This form may be reproduced.

Following Directions - Worksheet E

Name:_____ Date:_____

Copyright © 1997 by Academic Communication Associates. This form may be reproduced.

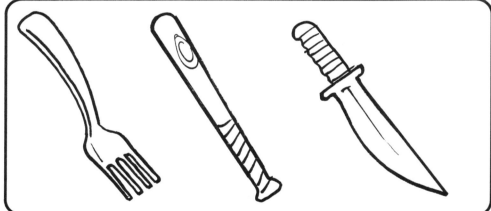

Appendix B
Gameboard Activities

This appendix includes two gameboards and three sets of reproducible playing cards:

      Card Set 1 - Animals
      Card Set 2 - Food
      Card Set 3 - Assorted Nouns

Each page includes nine playing cards. Reproduce the gameboards and the sheets with playing cards. Cut out the individual playing cards and put them in a stack.

The players take turns drawing cards and responding to the questions on these cards. Allow the child to move his/her marker one space following each correct response. The child earns one point each time that the marker reaches the final space on the board. The player with the most points at the end of the session is declared the winner.

Gameboard #1 - Copyright © 1997 by Academic Communication Associates. These pictures may be reproduced.

176

Gameboard #2 - Copyright © 1997 by Academic Communication Associates. These pictures may be reproduced.

Card 1

1. A pig says _____.

2. Does a pig live on a farm, a beach, or a branch?

3. Is a pig smaller or larger than an elephant?

4. Do we get beef or pork from a pig?

Card 2

1. Is a mouse loud, quiet, or noisy?

2. Does a mouse live in the ocean, sky, or on land?

3. Is a mouse smaller or larger than a pig?

4. Does a mouse like to eat cheese, meat, or bugs?

Card 3

1. A cat says _____.

2. Does a cat live in a refrigerator, car, or house?

3. Is a cat smaller or larger than a squirrel?

4. Does a cat chase a mouse, alligator, or elephant?

Card 4

1. A cow says _____.

2. Does a cow live in a house, barn, or tree?

3. Is a cow larger or smaller than a dog?

4. Do we get soda, juice, or milk from a cow?

Card 5

1. A frog says _____.

2. Does a frog live in the desert, a bowl, or a pond?

3. Is a frog larger or smaller than a fly?

4. Does a frog catch bugs with his feet, tongue, or hands?

Card 6

1. A dog says _____.

2. Does a dog live in a washing machine, house, or jar?

3. Is a dog larger or smaller than a hippopotamus?

4. Does a dog use fingers, claws, or paws?

Card 7

1. A horse says _____.

2. Does a horse live on a ranch, roof, or bed?

3. Is a horse larger or smaller than a wolf?

4. Do you need a chair, car, or a saddle to ride on a horse?

Card 8

1. A duck says _____.

2. Does a duck swim in milk, soda, or water?

3. Is a duck smaller or larger than a giraffe?

4. Does a duck flap its arms, legs, or wings?

Card 9

1. A snake says

_____.

2. Does a snake live in a house, forest, or office?

3. Is a snake larger or smaller than a lion?

4. Does a snake walk or crawl on its belly?

Card Set 1 - Animals   Copyright © 1997 by Academic Communication Associates. This page may be reproduced.

Card 1

1. Do mice or snakes like cheese?

2. Do you eat or drink cheese?

3. Name three foods you eat with cheese.

4. Is cheese yellow or blue?

Card 2

1. Is a lemon sweet or sour?

2. Is a lemon the same color as a banana or an orange?

3. Is a lemon a fruit or a vegetable?

4. Is a lemon larger or smaller than a grape?

Card 3

1. Is jelly sweet or sour?

2. Name three kinds of jelly.

3. Is jelly slippery or rough?

4. Does jelly come in a box or a jar?

Card 4

1. Is pizza covered with sand and gravel or sauce and cheese?

2. Is pizza usually round or square?

3. Name three things that you might put on a pizza.

4. Is the bottom of the pizza called the floor or the crust?

Card 5

1. Do most people eat eggs for breakfast, lunch, or dinner?

2. Is an egg larger or smaller than a cantaloupe?

3. Do eggs come from a dog or a chicken?

4. Name some foods that you eat with eggs.

Card 6

1. Does spaghetti look like a rock or string?

2. Name two things that you put on spaghetti.

3. Is spaghetti usually eaten for breakfast or dinner?

4. Do you eat spaghetti with a knife or a fork?

Card 7

1. Is a watermelon a vegetable, meat, or fruit?

2. Is the inside of a watermelon the same color as a lemon or a tomato?

3. Is a watermelon larger or smaller than a banana?

4. Is a watermelon heavier or lighter than an apple?

Card 8

1. Is bread hard or soft?

2. Is a waffle or toast made out of bread?

3. Do you make a sandwich or a cake out of bread?

4. Name two things that you spread on bread.

Card 9

1. Is corn the color of the sun or the sky?

2. Is corn grown on a playground or a farm?

3. Does corn grow on a vine or a cob?

4. Name something that is made out of corn.

Card 1

1. Is a washing machine used for dishes, clothes, or furniture?

2. Do washing machines have motors or batteries?

3. Do you put clean or dirty clothes in a washing machine?

4. Do you dry clothes in an oven or dryer?

Card 2

1. Do you use a refrigerator for milk or potato chips?

2. Does a refrigerator keep things cold or hot?

3. Name four items you have in your refrigerator.

4. Is a refrigerator larger or smaller than an oven?

Card 3

1. What do you do with a book?

2. Are there pages or petals in a book?

3. Are the pages in a book made of cheese or paper?

4. Is a book larger or smaller than a truck?

Card 4

1. Do you wear a hat on your arms or on your head?

2. Does a football player wear a beanie or a helmet?

3. Name three types of hats.

4. Name three people who wear hats with their uniforms.

Card 5

1. Do you wear a shoe on your hand or your foot?

2. Do you wear a sock or a glove with a shoe?

3. How many shoes do you wear on your feet?

4. Why do you wear shoes?

Card 6

1. Do you wear a jacket when it is warm or cold outside?

2. Does a jacket cover your legs or your arms?

3. Is a jacket a food, vegetable, or piece of clothing?

4. Does a jacket go over or under your shirt?

Card 7

1. Do you write with an eraser or a pen?

2. Is a pen filled with ink or juice?

3. Do you use a pen with a rock or piece of paper?

4. Is a pen larger or smaller than a toaster?

Card 8

1. Do you use scissors for sawing or cutting?

2. Are scissors dull or sharp?

3. Name two things that you cut with scissors.

4. Do you use scissors or a knife to cut steak?

Card 9

1. Does a car have pedals or an engine?

2. Does a car have two or four wheels?

3. Is a car a form of transportation or a fruit?

4. Does a car need gas or soda to go?

Card Set 3 - Assorted Nouns Copyright © 1997 by Academic Communication Associates. This page may be reproduced.